teaching science
with
everyday things

McGRAW-HILL BOOK COMPANY

NEW YORK   ST. LOUIS   SAN FRANCISCO   TORONTO   LONDON   SYDNEY

TEACHING

science

WITH EVERYDAY THINGS

VICTOR E. SCHMIDT
PROFESSOR OF SCIENCE, STATE UNIVERSITY OF NEW YORK

VERNE N. ROCKCASTLE
PROFESSOR OF SCIENCE EDUCATION, CORNELL UNIVERSITY

ILLUSTRATIONS BY RAYMOND F. HOULIHAN

**teaching science
with everyday things**

Copyright © 1968 by McGraw-Hill, Inc.
All Rights Reserved. Printed in the United
States of America. No part of this publi-
cation may be reproduced, stored in a
retrieval system, or transmitted, in any
form or by any means, electronic,
mechanical, photocopying, recording, or
otherwise, without the prior written permission of the publisher.

Library of Congress Catalog Card Number
68–13525

1234567890 BABA 7543210698

preface

This small book is designed to be of practical help to teachers, particularly those in the elementary school, and to college students who are preparing to teach. It requires no previous background in science, nor does it call for special or costly equipment. But it *does* assume a willingness to try new things, explore the fascinating world around us, and to seek answers in observations and experiments instead of merely accepting what others say. Above all, it asks, on the part of the reader, a desire to help children to do all these things.

Three underlying themes run through the book:

1. The foundation of all learning in science is firsthand experiences with real things.
2. Science experiences need not involve unusual, elaborate, or expensive apparatus and materials.
3. Investigating one's environment is an interesting and integral part of an education.

Anyone who expects to find in this book a treatment of atomic particles, chemical bonds, DNA, galaxies, or the earth's interior is bound to be disappointed. The material that *is* presented deals with things much closer at hand—things that children can watch and touch and try for themselves—and this material hardly requires abstract formulas and complex terminology. However, this is not to say that the science in the book is of a level beneath the dignity and intelligence of college students and college graduates. On the contrary, the principles and approaches developed in the book are basic to the study of science, regardless of level.

A book of this size can, at best, merely touch on some aspects of science and on some procedures useful in teaching science to children. Nevertheless, it includes enough subject matter and teaching suggestions to help teachers—especially those with little background—to teach science effectively and to grow in skill and confidence.

In writing this book, we have drawn upon a combined half-century of experience in teaching science and in working with teachers and with college students preparing to teach.

We have consistently tried to emphasize new and original materials and techniques, but many of the ideas have come, probably often without our realizing it, from others. We are very conscious of our indebtedness to numerous persons—mostly our teachers, colleagues, and students—and wish it were possible to thank each one individually for his help. Perhaps our gratitude is best expressed by our desire to share with a larger audience any contributions we have made as a result of their inspiration and encouragement.

Victor E. Schmidt
Brockport, New Yo

Verne N. Rockca
Ithaca, New Y

contents

activities

in
explanation

The twelve chapters which follow contain suggestions of instructional activities in science presented especially for the elementary school teacher or prospective teacher who may lack confidence in teaching science or whose background in science is limited. Space permits the inclusion of only a sampling of activities. However, these are of sufficient number and variety to illustrate sound approaches useful in teaching science at any grade level. They involve many of those processes and principles on which the most modern elementary science programs are based.

In each chapter the introduction is followed by a listing of some important objectives, and these, in turn, are followed by the activity suggestions. There is no special significance to the order of the chapters. The teacher may begin with any one or anywhere within one. Consequently, the book can be used in connection with any elementary science program or text— or in the absence of either.

The following comments are intended to help the teacher use this book more effectively:

POINTS OF VIEW:
These present some fundamental philosophical considerations and general suggestions for making science teaching effective and pleasant. In some ways the most important part of the book, they should be reread from time to time and considered carefully insofar as they apply to any particular class and school.

OBJECTIVES:
A sampling of important objectives toward which the teaching should be directed is presented in each area. For the most part these are attainable, to some degree at least, by means of the activities suggested in that area. However, it should be emphasized that these objectives are stated for the teacher's guidance only; they should not be taught directly.

GRADE PLACEMENT:

The activities in each area are suggested in approximate order of increasing difficulty, from simple ones generally suitable for the lower grades to more complex for the higher. Specific grade placement is avoided, however, because it might unduly bias the teacher. For one thing, simple activities are often helpful, even in the upper grades, for children with limited experience, while in some instances capable primary pupils may be ready to try some relatively difficult ones.

QUESTIONS:

Examples of questions to be asked of pupils are printed in *italics*. The purpose of these questions is to encourage pupils to observe and think carefully, and the questions should be modified and augmented as needed. No answers are given, because observation and thought—not the book or the teacher—should be the source of the answers.

MATERIALS:

Practically all the items suggested are common and easily available. Many can be salvaged from waste; others can be purchased locally. Substitute items often serve equally well, and pupils can suggest alternative possibilities. Occasionally, changes in materials and packaging will make some things less easy to obtain, but then replacements for them can likely be found.

ASSISTANCE:

Custodians, science teachers, older students, and parents can provide materials and assistance. However, the teacher must make certain that they, in trying to be helpful, do not hinder good teaching by introducing unnecessarily elaborate equipment, too complex subject matter and terminology, or premature answers.

DIFFICULTIES:

On occasion, an activity may not "work." This could mean that something new has been discovered. Or it may be because the materials or techniques used are different from those the authors had in mind. It is usually best for the teacher to try things himself first, with no pupils present. Then, in case of difficulty, he should reread the directions carefully, paying special attention to materials and techniques—and try again!

teaching science
with
everyday things

counting
and
measuring

1

Among the most important skills to be developed in the elementary school are those involved in communication. To communicate with others, a pupil must be able to describe accurately what he observes. Also, he must be able to understand the accounts of others. Counting and measuring are important contributions to such communication.

As pupils share experiences, they will find themselves comparing objects and events. Comparison implies counting and measuring. So, in a pupil's study of science he will rely increasingly upon his own and his classmates' ability to count and to measure.

Man's progress has been due, in large part, to his ability to measure with greater and greater precision. A part for a modern machine must be close-fitting, and its replacement must be nearly identical. The amount of medicine in a pill, the curvature of a lens, and the uniformity of synthetic fibers all require precise measurements. Young pupils will not need this degree of precision in their explorations, but they can appreciate the need for precision and refinement of technique even in simple activities.

The suggested activities should not be considered ends in themselves. Instead, they are means to an understanding of measurement, illustrating the kinds of experiences children should have. The devices described are not gadgets; they are instruments for the pupils to use in investigating their environment.

Just as learning to read a thermometer is a step toward understanding weather, making a saw-blade balance is a step toward a general understanding of how weight can be measured. Finding the weight of a slice of apple should never become the primary objective of the teacher, even if it is the primary objective of the pupil. For the teacher, it should merely illustrate a method of obtaining information. Subsequently, the child's understanding of measurement should be broadened and deepened by further experiences.

SOME IMPORTANT OBJECTIVES

ATTITUDES AND APPRECIATIONS TO BE ENCOURAGED:

Events or objects are better described if they can be counted or measured.

Measurements are never exact, but some are more nearly exact than others.

Some measurements must be made with more precision than others, depending upon their purpose.

When measuring, one should be honest and careful and as precise as one's instruments will permit.

Indirect measurements can be as accurate and useful as direct measurements.

No one system of units is inherently more accurate than another, but some, such as the metric system, are more convenient to use.

Good measuring instruments are important, and deserve the care of important things.

A measurement checked several times by several observers is better than one taken only once or by one observer.

A single system of units is desirable because it would make international communication easier and more meaningful.

SKILLS AND HABITS TO BE DEVELOPED:

Holding and reading to the smallest division simple devices to measure distance (rulers, meter sticks, folding rules, etc.)

Reading various scales at right angles so as to avoid parallax

Weighing objects and timing events with speed and accuracy

Changing measurements in one unit (such as meter) to another unit in the same or different system (such as centimeter or inch)

Finding the arithmetic average of several measurements or counts

Estimating, with a fair degree of accuracy, various distances, weights, and times

Visualizing units such as square inches in a square foot, square centimeters in a square meter, and cubic feet in a cubic yard

Finding the dimensions of very small objects either by using indirect means or by combining the dimensions of several and dividing by the number involved

FACTS AND PRINCIPLES TO BE TAUGHT:

Dimensions of ordinary measurement are distance, mass, and time. Most common measurements are one or a combination of these.

Measures of any object are really comparisons with other objects of known or accepted dimensions.

In order for people to communicate measurements to one another and to understand what they mean, they need standards for comparison. International standards are carefully made and protected.

When a wheel or some other object makes one turn in rolling along, it travels as far as the distance around its outer edge.

Weight is a measure of the attraction between an object's mass and the earth. If two objects on scales are "balanced," the attraction between the earth and each of the objects is the same; so the objects are of equal weight.

The weight of an object can also be found by measuring how much it stretches or bends something springy.

The number of swings a pendulum makes in a certain length of time depends mostly on its length and hardly at all upon its weight or the length of its swing.

TALLER
OR WIDER?

When people stretch their arms out in opposite directions, are they wider than tall or taller than wide? It will be an interesting experience for your pupils to write their opinions and then test them by measuring everyone in the class.

How many think that tall, slender persons are taller than wide? Wider than tall? Equal? What about short, stout persons?

Divide the class into teams, each with a tape recorder or a reporter who will write down as many as he can of the comments made by pupils as they investigate and a recorder to take down the measurements. When all the measurements have been made, let the class listen to the taped account (or written report) of how they went about the investigation, how they collected their data, and whether they became more precise in their observations and methods of measuring as they went along.

Ask each team to describe how they ensured that measurements were uniformly made and whether they made any changes along the way to minimize errors. *Were any measurements made before asking that shoes be removed? How was the top of each person's head projected against the wall so his height could be measured? If a book was used, how was it held to make sure it was kept level?*

Ask the pupils if it makes a difference whether the subject is standing or lying down. *Will his measurements be the same in the morning as in the late afternoon? Does age or sex make a difference?*

Pupils often are quick to generalize on the basis of a small sample. (*Everyone* does it! or *All* the kids have them!) Measuring whether

people are taller than wide or wider than tall will almost surely make the pupils more critical of first guesses. It will make them suspicious of data not carefully collected or of data collected for one group and then generalized to include other groups. It will also make them reluctant to generalize without plenty of evidence.

WHEEL MEASURE

Pupils have many opportunities to measure and to become adept at estimating short distances. But longer ones—such as those around the school, parking lot, or block— are not only difficult to estimate but require considerable time to measure with a ruler or tape. However, pupils can have fun measuring long distances quickly and fairly accurately by means of wheels. Let them write down how far they think it is from one end of the school building to the other and then check it as a part of this activity.

Ask that a few bicycles or tricycles be brought to school. Divide the class into groups, each with a bicycle, a tape measure or a string and yardstick, and a piece of chalk. Take them to a sidewalk or parking lot and there let each group measure some distances as follows:

Stand the bicycle upright and let someone make a mark on the tire where it touches the pavement and another mark directly next to it on the pavement. Then push the bicycle in a straight line until the chalk mark on the tire meets the pavement again, and mark this place. *How far apart are the two chalk marks on the pavement, in feet? In inches? In centimeters? How does this distance compare with that around the outside of the wheel? Measure to be sure. From your measurements, how far would the bicycle wheel travel in 10 turns? In 100 turns?*

It is easier for a bicycle rider to count the number of turns a pedal makes than to count the turns a a wheel makes. Therefore, let each group repeat the above activity but this time find out how far the bicycle travels for each complete turn of the pedals.

As an after-school activity, each pupil can record on a piece of tape stuck to his handlebars how far his bicycle travels for each turn of his pedals. Finding distances by bicycle can be useful in many instances, such as "Sound Bounce."

SWINGING
SECOND-TIMER

A most useful tool in science is a device for measuring time accurately. Pendulums work well for this. It is good to have at hand some that swing exactly once a second. Each pupil can have the fun of making and using one of his own, as follows:

Tie a piece of thread to a metal washer or nut, and knot a loop at its other end. Stick a pin halfway into the edge of a thick book, between the pages. Lay the book on a desk so that the pin is over the edge. Then hang the loop on the pin so that the pendulum can swing freely without hitting anything.

Pull the pendulum 2 or 3 inches to one side, and let it go when a "Timekeeper" says "Ready. Set. Go!" *How many complete (back and forth) swings does it make before he calls "Stop!" after exactly one minute?* Check this again and record it.

Perhaps only one or two of the pendulums made by a whole class will happen to swing just 60 times in one minute. Those which do not

do so may be changed until they *do* make one swing a second. *Does a pendulum swing less often if it swings harder, so that it has to go farther on each trip?*

A pendulum like this is disturbed by wind. Therefore, for use outdoors hang it in a gallon jug, putting the thread through a tiny nail hole in the cap and taping it on top.

With this instrument one can answer many questions, such as:

1. *How fast can toy trains or cars go, in feet per second?*

2. *Do drivers obey the speed signs near the school?* (At 15 miles per hour a car goes 110 feet in five seconds; at 25 miles per hour, 183 feet.)

3. *How fast does sand settle in water?* (See "Sorted Stones.")

4. *What is the speed of sound in air?* (See "Sound Bounce.")

5. *Does the length of time a candle burns when covered by a jar depend on the volume of the jar?* (See "Flame life Expectancy.")

TRIPLE-CAN BALANCE

Man has used balances for thousands of years to compare the weight of objects. They are still valuable tools of science. A very simple kind can be made and used by pupils, as follows:

Get a large, undented juice can which has been opened by punctures. Remove the label, and wash and dry the can well. Then stand two smooth blocks of wood of equal height on edge on a table. Be sure they are level. Lay the can on its side, with its edges on the blocks, so that it can roll freely.

Next, tape a large nail to the can, opposite the seam, so that when the can rolls, its seam comes to the top. Then drape two pieces of string over the can and tie their ends to nail holes in shallow cans of equal weight so that they hang freely and balance. Tape the center of each string to the seam of the large can.

To compare the weight of two things, simply place them in the hanging cans. To find the approximate weight of an object, put it in one can and add weights to the other until the two cans balance and the seam of the large can is at the top. Nails of the same size may be used for weights. Or a set of weights may be made by tying together various numbers of iron washers so that they balance weights from a science room.

Paper cups or paper bags may be substituted for the hanging cans. Also, the large can may be set on two level, smooth-top tables or desks placed a few inches apart, instead of on blocks.

This balance may be used to answer many questions, such as:

1. Which is heavier, a can of sand or an equal volume of water?

2. What kind of candy bar gives the most candy for a nickel?

3. How heavy are the candy bars? (A new nickel weighs 5 grams.)

4. Which weighs more, a sponge or the water it can soak up?

5. What does a pint of water weigh? (See "Units to Use.")

SAW-BLADE BALANCE

Although every classroom should have ready access to a commercial balance, it is often desirable for each pupil to have his own—one simple enough for him to make, yet inexpensive and sturdy. One such balance can be made from a hacksaw blade and a large can.

Insert a paper fastener through the hole in one end of the blade. Lay the saw blade across the top of the can, hold the paper fastener solidly in place with a strip of 1/2-inch adhesive tape, and turn up a bit of the fastener as shown. Fasten the blade at the opposite side of the can's rim with a piece of string and a second piece of tape. Then weight the can with sand or water.

Use a small paper cup for a weighing pan. Cut three pieces of string 4 inches long. Make three equally spaced holes near the rim of the cup, and tie a string at each. With the cup held *level*, run the strings up through the hole in the free end of the blade and tie a simple knot in all three strings at once. Finally, glue a paper strip to a second can and stand it next to the paper cup.

Before the balance can be used, it will first need to be *calibrated*. This means that a series of equal weights such as washers will have to be added to the cup, one at a time, and marks made on the paper strip where a particular point on the cup's rim comes as each weight is added. Then, when an unknown weight is placed in the cup, its weight in terms of the *standard* (washers) can be found by noting where the point on the rim of the cup meets the paper strip.

A balance of this sort might be used to tell how much of an apple or a potato is water. First, calibrate the balance in terms of washers or some similarly acceptable standard unit of weight. Then put a fresh slice of apple in the cup and weigh it (in terms of washers). Let the slice dry for a few days; then weigh it again. *How much weight did it lose? What fraction (or percentage) of its original weight does this represent? How much of an apple is water?*

QUARTS
AND
QUASI-QUARTS

Most pupils know what a quart is—a quart of milk, a quart of ice cream, a quart of strawberries. *Yet are all these "quarts" the same? Are they actually* quarts?

First show pupils how to use a measuring cup accurately. Fill it nearly up to a mark with water, and stand it so that it is level. Hold your eyes even with the mark, and slowly add water until the *flat surface* of the water is at the exact level of the mark.

Now have several pupils, in turn, each measure a quart of water into the same "quart" bottle, which should have a long narrow neck, and mark the level on a strip of adhesive tape. Provide a funnel so that no water is lost. *Do their measurements all agree?*

Then let others test different measuring cups. *Do the cups agree? Are 4 cups, or 2 pints, measured separately, exactly equal to 1 quart? Is a measuring cup just as accurate when held in one's hand as when resting on a level surface?*

Also have pupils check milk cartons and bottles. *Do these containers hold exact quarts? Do some hold more than others? How accurate are "quart" preserving jars and "gallon" jugs?*

Along the same lines, let pupils investigate such questions as:

1. *Do "quart" ice cream containers have the same volume as "quart" milk cartons or bottles? How about "pint" cartons and bottles?*

2. *How much do "quart" berry baskets hold? Get several, line them with sheet plastic, and measure water into them.*

3. *Just what is a quart? How does the dictionary define quart? Does a "dry" quart have the same volume as a "liquid" quart?*

4. *How could one test a measuring cup at home to see how accurate it is?*

5. *How might measuring cups be designed to make them more accurate than they are and still convenient to use?*

STANDARDS
OF MEASUREMENT

To show pupils that there is nothing sacred about systems of measurement, let them develop a system of their own and use it. This will help them to appreciate how our own conventional units were developed, what their limitations are, and how the systems we use depend on a few standards chosen more or less arbitrarily.

First, let the pupils select some object as a *standard* unit of length. It may be a blackboard panel, a stick, or a piece of paper. Let them give it a name, too, such as a "gort." Then let each pupil make his own copy of the standard gort from string or paper.

For a unit of weight, the pupils should decide on another standard. It may be an eraser, a particular block of wood, or a gort of clothesline. It, too, should have a name, such as "lob." Once the lob has been established, it can be set on a balance, and another lob made by filling a bottle with sand until it balances the standard. In a similar manner, 2-lob, 5-lob, and 10-lob weights can be made. *How can a 1/2-lob or a 1/10-lob weight be made?*

A "blip" may be the time required for one swing of a pendulum that is 1 gort long. (See "Swinging Second-timer.") For a longer time interval, a small hole can be punched in the bottom of a container. Then the container can be filled with water to a level that will take, say, 100 or 1,000 blips to empty.

When the system of units is established, it will become apparent that it is based on a few objects chosen arbitrarily. If these were lost, it would be difficult to reconstruct the system. For this reason,

the class should consider keeping their standards in the office safe (their Bureau of Standards). It will also be apparent that descriptions of objects in terms of the standards that the pupils have established are possible only if other people know about gorts, lobs, and blips. That is why a single system for all people is desirable.

Units of measurement often give pupils—and adults, too—trouble, chiefly because they are not used enough. Even units that are customarily studied are often not available in classrooms and therefore cannot be used or referred to easily.

To help pupils become more familiar with common units, have them make a collection for ready use and reference, like utensils in a well-ordered kitchen. Let them decide on a few units to start with and then add more as the need arises.

Some examples of useful units and measuring devices, many of them applicable to the activities in this book, are:

1. Ten-foot and longer chains or ropes. (Inexpensive chain from a hardware store, or rope, cut to length while pulled taut, and labeled. Such a chain, however, should not be confused with a standard *chain* used by surveyors, which is 66 feet long.)

    Can you mark off 1 acre of land on the school grounds? A square-shaped acre is very nearly 209 feet on each side.

2. One-meter sticks. (Yardsticks extended by pieces of scrap wood taped on to make them 39 3/8 inches long; also, pieces of scrap wood sawed to this exact length and labeled.)

    The world's record for running 100 meters is 10 seconds. *How fast can you run this distance?*

3. Metric rulers marked off in centimeters and millimeters.
    How long and wide, in centimeters and millimeters, is a 3- by 5-inch card? How tall are you in centimeters?

4. Square yards of cardboard, wallboard, or linoleum. (A square piece 1 yard on a side; also a few rectangular pieces of various shapes, all with areas of 1 square yard, labeled.)

    How many square feet are there in a square yard? Square inches? Square centimeters? Let pupils mark them off.

5. A cubic yard of air. (A cube outlined by twelve 1/4-inch dowel sticks, 36 inches long [from a lumber yard or hardware store], their ends slotted with a coping saw and stuck into eight Tinkertoy connectors at the corners; or a cube of 12 yardsticks with their ends glued to corners cut from cardboard cartons.)

    About how many children could fit in a cubic yard?

6. A cubic centimeter of potato, foam plastic, or soft wood. (A cube cut carefully so that each edge is 1 centimeter long.)

Is the volume of a sugar cube more or less than 1 cubic centimeter? How many cubic centimeters could be stacked in 1 cubic meter?

7. A bushel basket, peck basket, and quart basket, all labeled.
   How many apples are there in a bushel? In a peck? Let pupils estimate and then count.

8. Household measuring cups, quart-size and smaller; also a bottle graduated in fluid ounces, and measuring spoons.
   How many fluid ounces make 1 pint? What does 1 pint of water weigh?

9. A 1-liter and a 1/2-liter bottle. ("Quart" and "pint" bottles that actually hold 34 and 17 fluid ounces, both labeled.)
   In France milk is sold by the liter. *About how many liters of milk would your family use in a day?*

10. A 5-pound and a 10-pound jug. (Plastic jugs containing enough sand to make them weigh this much, labeled).

Do household and other scales all read alike when tested with these jugs?

11. A 1-kilogram and a 1/2-kilogram stone. (A stone or piece of brick or concrete that happens to weigh the same as 1 liter of water and another that is just half this heavy, both labeled.)
    Which would last longer in your home, 1 kilogram of butter or 2 pounds?

12. A set of weights, in grams. (Coat-hanger wire cut so that one piece weighs the same as two new nickels—10 grams; another, of identical kind and length, marked into 10 equal parts and then cut at the first, third, and fifth marks. This makes weights of 1, 2, 2, 5, and 10 grams. They may be bent into sections to indicate their values—the 2-gram weights, for example, in half.)
    How much does a marble weigh, in grams? A penny?

SQUEEZE PLAY

Scientists often need to measure things so tiny that ordinary measuring instruments are not of much use until many of the tiny things are added together. Finding the thickness of paper is one illustration of this; measuring reaction time is another.

Ask the class to form a line around the room and hold hands. Stand at one end of the line and clasp the hand of the child next to you. In your other hand hold a watch with a sweep second hand. Explain that you are going to squeeze the hand of the child next to you when the second hand gets to the top of the dial. When he feels your squeeze, he should squeeze the hand of his neighbor, and so on to the end of the line. The last child to feel the squeeze should immediately slap a desk or make some signal to you so that you can check the time.

After a practice run, measure how long it takes for the series of squeezes to travel the length of the line. If it takes 10 seconds from your squeeze to the last pupil's signal and if there are 20 pupils in the line, the average reaction time is 1/2 second per pupil (10 seconds divided by 20 pupils). *What would be the average reaction time if 7 seconds were required for the squeeze to be passed along by 28 children?*

Let the pupils repeat the exercise five times with their eyes closed so that they react only as they *feel* the squeeze. For each trial, record the reaction time. *How does the time vary as the activity is repeated? What are some reasons for the change?*

Have each pupil make his own graph of these five trials, showing reaction time versus the number of trials. *Is the graph a straight line?* From the graph, let each pupil estimate what would be the time for the tenth trial. *How does each one's estimate compare with the actual time obtained on the tenth trial? How many trials are needed before the reaction time seems to remain unchanged by additional trials?*

science
and
children

Children live in a world of science and during their entire lives will encounter scientific matters. As adults, they will help to make many decisions involving science—on wilderness conservation, pollution abatement, highway safety, urban planning, and population control—and to pay for scientific research and exploration. They will use innumerable "scientific" devices and work at jobs that depend, directly or indirectly, on science.

It is imperative, therefore, that citizens be scientifically literate and that pupils being educated for citizenship become functionally acquainted with science and the processes of science.

Fortunately, science is naturally appealing to children. It often is their favorite study. Should they develop a dislike for it, the reason probably lies neither in the subject nor in the children, but rather in the way the two are brought together.

Science is an excellent medium for teaching far more than mere facts. It can help pupils learn to organize their ideas and to think logically. It can serve as a means of teaching reading, writing, and arithmetic. It is ideally suited for developing honesty, cooperation, and respect for the opinions of others. And there is no subject area to which science cannot contribute!

Above all, good science teaching leads to what often is called a "scientific attitude." Having it, a person is disposed to be curious about his environment and to seek answers from it, to be honest and objective, to be wary of hasty judgments and sweeping statements, to weigh evidence carefully, and to reach conclusions with caution. Far more important than facts, such an attitude should be developed in all pupils. It probably can be if the proper approach is used. But it must not be expected to appear automatically with the mere acquisition of information!

13

air
and
weather

2

Air is strange stuff to study in the elementary school classroom. Pupils cannot see it, smell it, or taste it, nor can they feel it or weigh it as they would a pebble. Yet air is one of the most essential substances in a pupil's environment. In spite of its being invisible, it *can* be investigated, and it is fun to do so.

Learning about air not only helps pupils to appreciate and understand the vital fluid in which they live and the weather that affects much of what they do but also helps to show them the methods of a scientist. In investigating an invisible substance, children can engage in the kind of organized groping a scientist must do when he probes the unknown.

At first, children should simply investigate what air is like and where it is found. For a beginner to feel that air is real, he must capture it, squeeze it, carry it, and sense its resistance to being pushed aside. He does not think of a room as being full if it has no furnishings and no people. A drawer is not full if there is "nothing" in it. It takes time and many experiences with air as sensible stuff before it becomes as real as a pebble.

Next, children should have ample opportunity to investigate movements of air, temperature and its changes, air pressure, and the role of moisture in the air. As basic understandings develop, pupils can study changes in weather and can begin to hypothesize causes and predict patterns.

Although some investigation and prediction of weather is desirable, it should not become a prime objective to make forecasters of pupils. Forecasting weather is a complicated business, one that even professionals find difficult and at which they are not always successful. Still, so much of human activity depends upon the weather that pupils should be aware of its changes and the cause of some of them, and may well try their skill at prediction in a modest way.

14

SOME IMPORTANT OBJECTIVES

ATTITUDES AND APPRECIATIONS TO BE ENCOURAGED:

Air is as important a natural resource as water or soil, and should be valued to the same extent; it should not be polluted or taken for granted.

Air and its moisture are responsible for some of the most awesome and beautiful displays in nature, including thunderstorms, hurricanes, rainbows, clouds, mirages, blizzards, and glaciers.

Activities such as flying kites, sucking milk through a straw, and skiing on snow would be impossible without air.

Weather is the result of naturally occurring events and is not dictated by some supernatural power that operates with caprice.

The social and economic development of any area depends largely upon the weather and climate of that area.

Those of us who rely on special clothing and heated homes cannot fully appreciate the extremes of weather faced by some people and by many plants and animals.

Man's understanding of weather and his ability to predict it depends in part upon careful observations and accurate records.

Weather forecasters are responsible people who try to understand complicated, incompletely understood processes, and as they learn more about causes of weather, their predictions will improve.

SKILLS AND HABITS TO BE DEVELOPED:

Reading accurately, to within one unit, the scales of thermometers and barometers

Recognizing air as a fluid that must be displaced when filling, or must be admitted when emptying, a container of liquid

Recognizing cumulus and stratus clouds and the weather usually associated with each

Constructing simple weather instruments such as wind vanes and using them in observing and recording the weather

Recognizing the factors affecting evaporation and arranging wet things to dry fastest or keeping moist things from drying out

Keeping accurate records of weather data and using them in making simple forecasts of local weather

Reading a newspaper weather map and recognizing major features such as fronts, air masses, and areas of precipitation

Using correctly terms such as atmosphere, volume, pressure, expansion, barometric pressure, evaporation, and condensation

FACTS AND PRINCIPLES TO BE TAUGHT:

Air is real stuff just as pebbles and water are.

Air can be squeezed into a small space, but the smaller the space, the more pressure it takes to do it.

Air fills almost all common spaces that seem empty, and before another substance can fill these spaces, the air must come out.

Air tends to expand when it warms and contract when it cools.

Like water or soil, air cannot be moved without effort, thus slowing things that move through it.

When air is compressed, its temperature rises; when it is allowed to expand, its temperature decreases.

The atmosphere exerts a surprising amount of pressure on all the things it surrounds.

Because cold air cannot contain so much water vapor as warm air, condensation may occur when moist air cools.

A cloud is visible evidence of a process; it is continually changing and is not a permanent object in the same sense as a stone.

The climate is most severe near the surface of the ground, and its effect on human beings is minimized by clothing and other protection which some plants and some other animals do not have.

Sets of weather conditions may recur from time to time and can, therefore, be recognized from past records.

BAG
OF WIND

It takes time and many experiences for young children to learn that air is real stuff like water, even though it cannot be seen. One interesting experience is to let each pupil catch and investigate some air in his own plastic sandwich bag, as follows:

Hold open the mouth of the bag and swish it through the air to fill it. Quickly close the mouth and twist it tightly to trap the air inside. Squeeze the trapped air. *What does it feel like?* Hold the twisted part tightly and sit on the bag. *Can air hold you up?* If your bag should break, fill another, but this time ask some classmates to put their bags, together with yours, under a large thin board or book. Sit on the board. *Can three or four bags of air hold you up better than one? How big a person do you think you could hold up if you had many strong bags of air?* Try it!

Look through your bag of air at a classmate. *Can you see him? Can he see you?* Open your bag a little bit and smell the air. *Do you smell anything different from the bag itself?*

Open the bag wide, hold it by the corners of the closed end, and dump out the air. Twist the neck shut again, all the way to the bottom of the bag. *Is any air left in the bag? How can you get all the air out?* Try it and see if it works.

Again, fill the bag with air. Close the mouth of the bag and take it outdoors. Open the bag and empty out the air. Fill it with outdoor air and bring it inside. *Can you be sure that none of the air from the room is still in the bag?* Do all the things with the bag of outdoor air that you did with classroom air. *In

what ways is outdoor air like classroom air? How is it different?*

Try filling the bag with samples of air from other places around the school. Get a bag of air from inside the desk, from inside an "empty" wastebasket (see "Empty or Full?"), and from the hall. *Is there any place where you cannot find air to fill the bag?*

EMPTY
OR FULL?

To most young pupils, a tumbler or other container that holds nothing visible is empty. But some simple and entertaining activities will show that even though pupils cannot see anything in it, an "empty" container may be full.

Divide the class into several groups, each of which has an aquarium or a plastic pail two-thirds full of water and a plastic tumbler. (Plastic will not scratch or crack the aquarium.) Give each pupil a drinking straw; then let each group proceed as follows:

Ask one pupil to put the tumbler in the water so that it fills completely. While it is under water, ask him to turn it bottom side up and lean it against the corner of the aquarium, holding it so that the open end stays tilted. Another pupil should insert the end of his drinking straw under the tilted tumbler and blow a bubble. *Where does it go? Is there as much water in the glass as before? If not, what does the glass contain besides water?*

While one pupil continues to hold the tumbler, the others should take turns blowing bubbles until it is only half full of water. *Now what does the tumbler contain—half water and half what else?*

When all the pupils in a group have added enough breath to the tumbler so that all the water has left it, let the one holding it remove it from the water, still keeping it bottom side up, and set it on a table. *What is in the glass now? Is it empty or full?*

Ask that the tumbler be turned right side up, slowly. *Does it look the same as when it was upside down? Even though it looks empty, what does it contain?* Let one pupil in each group invert the tumbler and push it down into the water so that the group can see how its invisible contents keep the water from entering.

Ask the class to look for other "full" containers that seem empty. *What is in an "empty" wastebasket? Can anyone find a really empty container?*

WEE BREEZES

Part of the experience of young pupils studying air should be to observe some ways in which air is made to move. They cannot see air, but they can see small, light objects move with it, and these help them to visualize what the air is doing.

Give each small group of pupils a flat sheet of stiff cardboard about 11 by 17 inches (such as comes in cartons of duplicating paper) and a handful of puffed rice. Ask them to lay the cardboard on a desk or the floor and sprinkle puffed rice around its edge. Then ask one of them to grip two edges of the cardboard and lift it quickly, keeping it level. *What happens to the puffed rice?* Let each pupil in the group try this several times. Then invite suggestions from all the pupils to explain why the puffed rice moved.

Ask the pupils to put the cardboard down again and sprinkle puffed rice around the edges as before. This time ask one pupil to raise, slowly, one end of the cardboard several inches and then let it go. *What happens to the puffed rice? Does the cardboard fall into* exactly *the same spot in which it lay before being raised?* Again, let each pupil have a try before inviting explanations.

Now sprinkle some puffed rice on the floor along the inside of a closed door. *What happens to the grains when the door is opened quickly?* Then, while it is open, replace the puffed rice along the threshold and quickly close the door. *Do the grains move the same way now as when the door was opened?*

In autumn, collect some fluffy seeds such as those of milkweed, cattail, or thistle. Put a few on each desk along both sides of an aisle and ask a pupil to walk past them. *What happens to the seeds?* Put some around a sheet of paper, as puffed rice was put around the cardboard; then try lifting it. *Can this be done without disturbing the seeds? Can any movement be made in air without causing a breeze?*

This helps to explain why air, even when it seems to be very still, may be in motion. Even a walking bug makes a wee breeze!

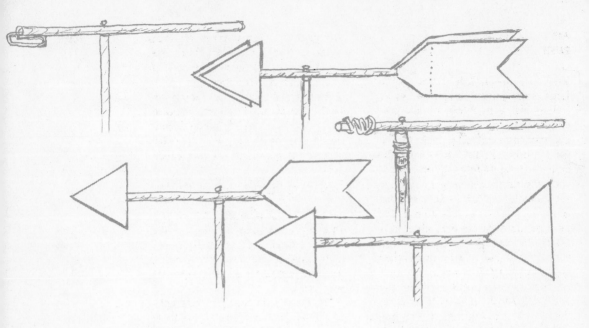

STRAWS
IN THE WIND

Unfortunately, some wind vanes shown in science books would not work if tried. They would not point *into* the wind, as they should, because of poor design. However, although such errors ought not to occur, they may be turned to good advantage if used to make pupils aware that books are not infallible.

To do this, and also to help pupils develop creativity and skill in analyzing how things work, let each one make a simple wind vane of his own invention from drinking straws, pins, paper clips, pencils, rubber bands, construction paper, paste, and such. Then go outdoors with them, away from buildings, when there is a steady breeze. Have them hold their wind vanes high.

Which ones work best—turn easily and consistently point into the wind? Why do some turn more freely than others? What makes some stay level and others keep one end low? Why do some point with the wind instead of into it? Why do some turn sideways to the wind?

Let the pupils experiment with their wind vanes and change them so that they work better. Then let them look at the wind vanes pictured in books, make some, and test them. *Can anyone tell, even before trying them, what should be done to some of these to improve them?*

A good wind vane has these characteristics:

1. It turns easily, readily showing changes in wind direction.

2. The area of the tail is larger than that of the head so that the wind exerts more force on it than on the head.

3. The tail extends farther from the pivot than the head does, and so, even if the force on it were the same as on the head, the turning effect would be greater. (See "Paper-clip Cranks.")

4. The head is weighted in order to balance the larger tail.

5. The tail may be double and spread apart slightly to make the vane steadier.

AIR
PUSH

With a wide-mouth gallon jar, a large, strong plastic bag that has no holes, and a few feet of string, a child can have truly fascinating experiences with the push of air. *Each* pupil should carry out the activities; a demonstration would spoil the fun. Gathering a complete set of materials for each individual requires effort, but the things can also be used for many other purposes. School cafeterias often can supply the jars, while pupils can bring the bags and string.

First, ask each pupil to fill his bag with air. Most pupils will blow up the bags. Show them that a bag can also be filled by pulling it through the air quickly with its mouth held open. (See "Bag of Wind.")

Next, let them help each other tie an air-filled bag upside down to a jar so that the mouth of the bag is over the mouth of the jar. They should wind the string around the bag and jar tightly three or four times *so that it does not cross the ridges of glass*, and then tie it *tightly* with a *bow* knot.

Then have them press down on the bag, lean on it, and rest a book on it. *Why doesn't it go down? What other things act like this?* Be sure pupils mention balloons, paper bags, and tires.

Now ask them to remove the bag and then tie its mouth *tightly* over the jar, just as before, except this time with the bag *inside* the jar. When everything is ready, have each one—*all at the same time*—hold his jar and pull the bag out. Surprise!

The reason is that the bag acts somewhat like a hammock with a person lying in it. To pull up the hammock, one has to lift not only the hammock itself but also the person in it. In like manner, the plastic bag has air resting on it—air that extends as far up as air goes, hundreds of miles. A pupil cannot lift this much air—it weighs several hundred pounds!

ONE-GALLON CLOUD

As a sequel to "Air Push" and with the same materials, a pupil can easily make a cloud. He need only set up conditions similar to those which often cause real clouds to form, as follows:

Pour a cup of water into a wide-mouth gallon jar. Then hold a lighted match in the jar, blow it out, and keep it there briefly. Next put a strong plastic bag, without holes, inside the jar and fold its top down over the rim of the jar. Or cut the neck from a large, round, rubber balloon and stretch the remainder over the rim. Fasten the bag or rubber *tightly* with a few turns of strong string tied with a *bow* knot or with several rubber bands.

Ask someone to hold the jar firmly on a table. Then pull up the bag or rubber—hard! A cloud, easily seen in bright light, forms in the jar, and then disappears when the bag is let go.

Can a cloud be made in the jar without using water? With water, but without smoke? Will other impurities, such as automobile exhaust fumes or frying-pan smoke, work in place of match smoke?

The cloud forms because of a chain of events. The air in the jar contains invisible water vapor and many extremely small particles from the match. This air is pressed upon by the air above the bag, but when the bag is pulled up, the pressure on it is reduced. As a result, it expands, and in doing so, becomes cooler. As the air cools, some of its water vapor changes to liquid water around particles from the match, forming thousands of minute droplets which are seen as the cloud.

Some kinds of real clouds, especially *cumulus* clouds, are formed in much the same way. When air moves to a region of lower air pressure, often as a result of rising, it expands and cools. Then some of its water vapor may condense on minute particles of impurities, forming tiny droplets. Not all clouds, however, are formed like this, nor do they all consist of water droplets.

BOTTLE
BAROSCOPE

Because of its weight, the air around us presses on everything it touches. A simple *baroscope,* or pressure indicator, shows pupils that this pressure changes much of the time, and makes it possible for them to keep a record of these changes.

Find a bottle with a long slender neck, such as a wine bottle or hairtonic bottle. Invert it in a pint or quart jar half full of water. Then have a pupil warm the bottle with both hands until several large bubbles of air escape. *What causes this to happen? Why does the water then rise as the bottle cools again?*

Stand the jar and bottle in a place where the temperature stays the same, as in a cabinet in a heated schoolroom. Place a thermometer near them, and have pupils check it frequently.

There is a sort of contest—a "push-of-war"—going on between the air inside the bottle and the air outside. The air inside pushes on the water in the neck of the bottle and tends to make it go down. The air outside connects with the air in the jar, and this air presses on the water in the jar, tending to make the water level rise in the neck of the bottle.

What will happen if the outside air presses harder? If its pressure becomes less? Can you see this happen during a day? Two days? It helps to have a scale. For this, number the lines on a large index card, bend the card around the jar, lined side in, and tape it on. Then pupils can read and record, from time to time, the level of the water inside the bottle.

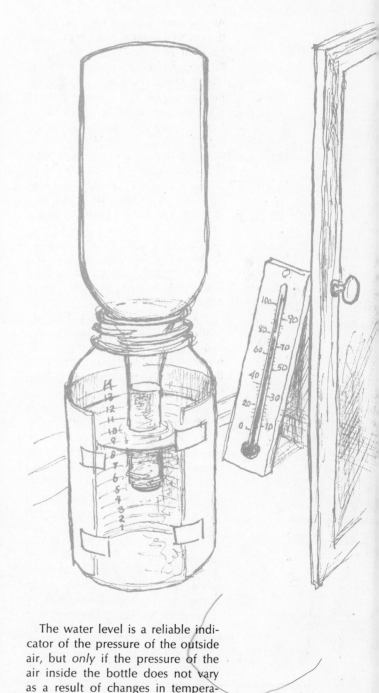

The water level is a reliable indicator of the pressure of the outside air, but *only* if the pressure of the air inside the bottle does not vary as a result of changes in temperature. This is why its temperature must be kept constant. *What happens when the bottle is warmed by being held or is cooled with ice?*

RAINFALL
MAGNIFIER

Pupils are generally aware of rain because it affects their activities, but they probably do not appreciate how varied the amount of rainfall can be. Some simple investigations of the depth of rainfall in containers will help to make them aware of these variations and of the wind direction, cloud forms, and pressure changes associated with rainy weather.

At the start, ask each pupil to bring to school a straight-sided, top-less container. See that the assortment includes metal cans, jars, and milk cartons, as well as a sand pail or plastic bucket with sloping sides and a cone-shaped beverage container. Let several of the class cut "empty" (see "Empty or Full?") milk cartons to half their normal height, each using one of these for his container. The rest should use containers from the assortment brought to school. Ask the class which of all the containers they think will collect the deepest water and which will collect the greatest volume of water during a rain. Let them try to rank the containers from most to least, giving reasons for their ranking.

On a rainy day, let each pupil carry his container, inverted, outdoors to an unprotected place and at a signal set it right side up on the ground to catch the rain. When the rain has stopped, or at the end of a particular time, such as an hour, the class should collect its containers for examination. As a signal was given for the containers to be set to catch rain, a signal can be given for them to be covered with cardboard so that the same period of time elapses for rain to fall into each.

In the classroom, each pupil should use a ruler to measure the depth of water in his container.

Which shape container has the deepest water? Which has the shallowest? Do all similar containers (quart milk cartons, for example) have the same depth of water? Does the container with the deepest water also contain the greatest volume of water?

To answer this last question, let each pupil in turn pour the rainwater from his container into a straight-sided olive bottle, marking the water level on a strip of adhesive tape fastened to the side. Which container did collect the greatest volume of water? Which had the least? Why is the rainwater deeper in the olive bottle than in the container that collected it?

Since most rainstorms drop only a fraction of an inch of water, it is easy to make big errors in its measurement. An observer who makes an error of 1/8 inch in measuring 1/4 inch of rainwater would make a 50 percent error (1/8 is half of

1/4). If there were 2 inches of rain-water, however, and the observer made the same error of 1/8 inch in measuring its depth, he would make a much smaller error (1/8 is only a sixteenth of 2). For this reason, a commercial rain gauge usually collects rain in a large-diameter can and pours it into a smaller-diameter one for measuring.

Now show each pupil how to make a simple rain gauge, as follows, using an olive bottle and a large juice can whose top has been removed. First, tape two straight pins to the flat side of a ruler so that the point of one projects exactly 1/2 inch farther than the other. Fill the can with water until the level comes just to the upper pinpoint, with the edge of the ruler resting across the mouth of the can. Then spoon water from the can into the bottle until the level drops to the lower pinpoint. On a strip of tape fastened to the outside of the bottle mark 1/2 inch

where the water level comes. Repeat the process, adding another 1/2 inch of water and marking 1 inch on the tape. *Where would 1/4 inch and 3/4 inch of "rainfall" be marked on the tape?*

To make a rain gauge that does not depend upon pouring water from a can into a bottle, set a funnel into the top of a large can to direct rainfall into a smaller one under the funnel's spout. The magnifying effect of such a gauge depends upon the area at the funnel's rim compared with that of the smaller can.

When the rain gauges have been completed, let the pupils set them outdoors in unprotected places to measure the rainfall in several storms. *How much rainfall does a thunderstorm deliver? Which gives more rainfall—a thunderstorm or an all-day drizzle? What combination of wind direction, air pressure, and cloud forms produces the most rain?*

THUNDERSTORM PATHS

To many persons a thunderstorm is a noisy, awesome thing that appears and disappears rather unpredictably. But these storms often move along in paths that your pupils can plot at school or at home.

Have each pupil prepare a plotting map in advance, using a large sheet of paper and a drawing compass. With the compass point at the center of the sheet, let him draw a series of concentric circles of 1, 2, 3, 4, 5, and 6 inches radius. The circles should be labeled "1 mile," "2 miles," and so forth, to represent distance from the pupil's position at the center of his map.

Next, have each pupil sketch the position of major land features on his map, including hills, large buildings, and waterways. As on most maps, north should be at the top of the sheet.

When thunder is heard, each pupil should move to a place where he can watch for lightning, placing his map so the north edge is toward the north. Each time he sees a lightning flash he should begin to count seconds (having practiced by using the "Swinging Second-timer") until he hears the thunder. Since sound travels approximately 1,100 feet per second in air, each five seconds that elapse between lightning and thunder means about a mile of distance. From the flash, he knows the direction to the storm, and from the delay in the arrival of the thunder, he can tell how far away it is.

For each lightning flash and subsequent clap of thunder, the pupil should make a dot on his map, labeling it "1" if it is his first observation, "2" if it is his second, and so on. Cloud-to-ground strikes will be easier to plot than cloud-to-cloud flashes.

Do the plotted points lie in a line, or do they skip around? How fast does the storm move, and in what direction? How wide is its path? Do not be surprised if curiosity and questions replace awe and fear on the part of the pupils who try this activity.

**objectives
and
outcomes**

To be good, science teaching must have well-defined objectives. The content and approach should lead to worthwhile outcomes and not be used just because of tradition or for the sake of novelty.

The more clearly a teacher has his purposes in mind, the more effectively he can teach. In fact, once he decides on definite objectives, planning how to attain them and how to evaluate the extent to which they are attained is greatly facilitated. For example, if his goal is to have youngsters learn how to connect simple electric circuits, his methods and materials are obvious. Or, if he wants them to appreciate the importance of checking measurements, his approach, again, is clear. But never does he have the pupils merely memorize statements of the objectives!

Examples of objectives are given in this book in three groups, and these are placed in their probable order of importance, thus:

ATTITUDES AND APPRECIATIONS TO BE ENCOURAGED:

There is a beautiful orderliness in the motions and the changes in appearance of the sun, moon, and stars.

No creature is, in itself, harmful or beneficial; it is so only in terms of how it affects man's well-being.

SKILLS AND HABITS TO BE DEVELOPED:

Making and using a simple compass to find magnetic direction

Working with others in carrying out an investigation and in gathering and analyzing data cooperatively

FACTS AND PRINCIPLES TO BE TAUGHT:

Sounds differ in pitch, which depends on their rate of vibration, or frequency.

Although earth materials and features are continually being changed, the same materials are often used again and again.

27

water and other liquids

3

Water is important to study, not only because it is essential for life, but because it is so abundant, covering three times as much of the earth's surface as does land and occurring in many places underground, in plants, and in our own bodies. Its buoyancy makes it possible to move people and cargoes by ship—without which early exploration and commerce could not have been accomplished. Hydroelectric installations are and for a long time will continue to be the major source of electrical energy. Water is also important for sanitation, irrigation, and recreation.

Childhood experiences with liquids should include those dealing with buoyancy, change of state, and surface films. Children should investigate under what conditions objects float or sink, both in water and other liquids, and should play in water with inner tubes or beach balls. They should watch ice melt and water freeze, evaporate, and condense. They should also observe other substances that change state easily, such as candle wax and butter.

In their investigations of liquids, pupils should become aware of the ease with which certain ones evaporate and of the dangers of fumes such as those from cleaning fluids and gasoline. They should experience the pleasure of playing in and around water but should also be made aware of the hazards and be taught to play safely.

Pupils must learn of man's increasing demands upon fresh water and develop a healthy concern for how it is used. The amount of water on earth does not change; the water is only recycled. What is used by pupils today is part of the same water used by dinosaurs.

Finally, pupils should come to appreciate the vastness of the sea and the method by which fresh water from it is transported to land areas. They should know the potential of the sea for additional fresh water, for food, and for chemicals, as well as its effect on weather, transportation, and recreation.

SOME IMPORTANT OBJECTIVES

ATTITUDES AND APPRECIATIONS TO BE ENCOURAGED:

Without water there can be no life—at least like that on earth—since water is the major constituent of cells and tissues.

Clean water is not unlimited; hence, no one has the right to pollute or waste it.

Most of the water used by a person or community must later be used by others; so every user should be considerate of his downstream neighbors.

As a burgeoning population demands increasing amounts of fresh water, man must look to the sea for extracting additional supplies.

Although fossil fuels and nuclear energy are important, the falling of water from dammed-up rivers and tides still is our most important source of electrical energy. At the same time, most of the earth's hydroelectric potential is as yet untapped.

Some of nature's most beautiful displays—rainbows, seascapes, waterfalls, and clouds—are a result of water.

Evaporation from the sea and subsequent precipitation over land is the means of replenishment of fresh water for drinking, sanitation, recreation, and irrigation and of falling water for hydroelectric power plants.

SKILLS AND HABITS TO BE DEVELOPED:

Keeping streams, lakes, and oceans free of litter and pollution

Being reluctant to waste tap water, even though the supply may seem limitless

Pouring liquids without spilling or splashing

Selecting the most absorbent material available and using it effec-tively when removing spilled liquids

Hastening the evaporation of a liquid by heating it, increasing its surface, or speeding the movement of air across it

Recognizing the buoyant force of liquids on objects and using it to advantage to float objects by increasing their displacement

Covering cold objects such as water pipes and iced drinks to avoid damage to furniture from condensation

Remembering to give water to pets, household plants, farm animals, and even wild birds as they need it

Using correctly terms such as fluid, displacement, buoyancy, change of state, vapor, condense, cohere, surface film, immiscible, pollution, sewage, and conservation

FACTS AND PRINCIPLES TO BE TAUGHT:

Water is rarely pure; it nearly always has other substances, even air, dissolved in it or mixed with it.

The tendency of some liquids to evaporate is so great that they exert considerable pressure in doing so.

Most substances are visible in their solid or liquid state, but not as vapors.

When a liquid evaporates, it leaves behind many of its impurities.

Liquids vary in their tendency to evaporate; under the same conditions, some evaporate faster than water, and some less rapidly.

Many substances that are normally solid become liquid at higher temperatures, and some even gaseous, while some that are gaseous at ordinary temperatures become liquid upon cooling. Water is one of the relatively few that are liquid at ordinary temperatures.

When two granular solids are mixed, the space they occupy apparently increases, but many granular solids dissolve in water with no appreciable change in the volume of the water.

Water and other liquids tend to cohere and thus to have a surface film that can support relatively heavy objects.

A liquid tends to buoy up an object immersed in it with a force equal to the weight of the liquid that the object displaces.

When objects of the same weight are compared, those with larger volumes have greater buoyancy.

Large animals such as whales and flimsy ones such as jellyfish can live only in water, which buoys them.

LIQUID LIFT

Is it easier to float in fresh or in salt water? For pupils who do not know the answer or who know but do not understand, the following investigation of the buoyancy of a pencil in fresh and in salt water may help.

Have the pupils gather several pencil stubs from 3 to 4 inches long and some olive bottles or toothbrush containers. (Supplement their collection with test tubes, if necessary.) Divide the class into small groups, seeing to it that each group has a pencil, an olive bottle, and a paper cup. Then let them proceed as follows:

Fill the bottle nearly full with tap water. Drop the pencil in it, eraser down. Holding the bottle vertically, tap it to free the pencil, and observe where the water line comes on its label. If the pencil leans and sticks to the side of the bottle, press a thumbtack into its eraser to make it float more nearly upright. *So long as the pencil floats freely, does the place where the water level comes on it change, even if the water level in the bottle is raised or lowered?*

Pour the water into the cup, add a teaspoonful of table salt, and stir until it dissolves. Refill the bottle and float the pencil once more. *According to where the water level comes on its label, does the pencil float higher, or lower, than before?* Add a second teaspoonful of salt. *What does this do to the buoyancy of the pencil?* Try a sample of sea

water (see "Super Solution") to see what it does to the buoyancy of the pencil.

What do you think it would be like to swim in very salty water such as Great Salt Lake or the Dead Sea? What would likely happen to a ship that sails from the sea into a body of fresh water such as the St. Lawrence River or the Great Lakes?

DIVING
DROPPER

This amazing device presents pupils with a fascinating problem, *What makes it work?* It is a simple form of a *Cartesian diver*, a toy often made of glass in the shape of a devil or diver.

To make one, fill a medicine dropper part way with water so that it *barely* floats in a tall glass of water. Only the tip of the bulb should stick out. Then, without squeezing the bulb, transfer the dropper to a tall bottle *completely* filled with water.

Now, when a pupil places his palm tightly over the mouth of the bottle and presses down on the water, the dropper sinks. When he lets go, it comes up again. With practice he can make the dropper dive, rise, or stay at any level he likes.

Its action may be explained in two ways, really not different:

1. The pressure of one's hand on the water causes a little more water to be pushed into the dropper. This can easily be seen. *How does this added water affect the weight of the dropper? What happens to the added water when the pressure is released? Then how is the weight of the dropper affected?*

2. The air inside the dropper is basically a bubble which tends to float because it is buoyed up by the water. The bigger this bubble, the more it is buoyed up. At first it is large and buoyant enough to keep the dropper afloat. *But what happens to its size when one presses on the water? Its buoyancy? How are its size and buoyancy affected when the pressure is released?*

Instead of pressing directly on the water, it may be easier for pupils to push on a piece of rubber balloon that is stretched over the mouth of the bottle and held tightly with rubber bands.

The principle illustrated by the diving dropper is used in submarines. These take in water to submerge, and force it out again with compressed air in order to come to the surface.

VAPOR PUSH

In "One-gallon Cloud," pupils learned one way that water gets *out* of the air. But water and some other liquids get *into* the air, too, as is shown by the pressure they create when they evaporate.

Give each group of about six pupils a gallon jar, some stout rubber bands, and a large balloon such as the ones which can be purchased in most five-and-tens. Have one pupil in each group cut the balloon to make a diaphragm that can be stretched across the mouth of the jar. Then ask the pupils to proceed as follows:

Pour about two tablespoonfuls of water into the jar and quickly stretch the rubber diaphragm over the opening. Fasten it firmly with the rubber bands. Now sight across the top of the jar. *Is the diaphragm perfectly flat?* Check it carefully at the end of each minute for five minutes. *Is it flat at the end of a minute? At the end of five minutes? What might account for this?*

Some pupils may suggest that the air in the jar has warmed and expanded, pushing up the rubber. Let each group empty and dry its jar, then try the activity once more. But this time, they should put a thermometer inside the jar. *Does the diaphragm bulge as before? Is this due to warming of the air?*

Now have them dry their jars thoroughly and replace the water with an equal amount of rubbing alcohol. *How does its effect on the diaphragm compare with that of water? How would two jars—one with water and one with alcohol— compare if left overnight?*

When water and other liquids evaporate, they take up more space.

Without any change in temperature, air with water vapor in it takes up more space than the air before water vapor is added. Suppose that the door and windows of a classroom are closed and the chalkboard is moistened. *Will any air be pushed out under the door as a result of the evaporation from the board?*

HOLEY SCOW

A lightweight aluminum pan, especially a rectangular one, makes a good barge, or scow, for pupils to experiment with.

Will such a scow float even if pricked with holes? If so, can it still carry a load of paper clips or small pebbles? Let pupils find out. Also encourage them to investigate these questions:

1. *How much weight can a holey scow support before sinking?*

2. *How numerous, or large, can the holes be before it sinks?*

3. *What happens to drops of water dripped on the holes?*

Have pupils look through a magnifying glass at the water in the larger holes. *How is its surface shaped? Does it look somewhat like a fingertip pressed into the hole in a washer?* The water acts as though it has a "skin" or film on its surface. This is because it holds together—it clings to itself, or *coheres.*

Now let *each* pupil do the following things and observe closely how, in each case, the water displays *cohesion* and a *surface film* which it has as a result of this cohesion:

1. Sprinkle a little water on a flat sheet of waxed paper.

2. Turn off a faucet gradually so the falling stream of water becomes thinner and thinner and then separates into drops.

3. Dip a strainer or wire screen into water, and lift it out.

4. Use some cloth to show how a person who falls in the water can trap air inside his wet shirt or trousers to keep afloat.

5. Lay a bit of aluminum foil on water; then push it under.

6. Rub a small needle with dry fingers, and float it on water by lowering it onto the surface with a U-shaped piece of wire.

7. Sprinkle dry sand grains on water; then try to sink them.

8. Watch water striders walking on water and denting it.

BENEATH THE SUDS

Most children know that soaps and detergents help to get rid of grease and oil on hands and dishes, but probably few know how they do it. With two *immiscible* (unmixable) liquids such as corn oil and water, and a small amount of detergent, pupils can find out for themselves what happens beneath the suds.

See that each pupil has a small, screw-cap glass jar, a toothpick, and a paper towel (in case of spilling). At one side of the room place several small jars containing corn oil and other cooking oil, each with a dropper, and a few jars containing small amounts of detergent. Ask each pupil to fill his own jar two-thirds full of water and add 10 to 20 drops of oil. Then have him take his jar back to his seat to investigate as follows:

Does the oil float, or sink, or does some float and some sink? If some is pushed underwater, what happens to it? If the oil is stirred gently, does it mix with water? Cover the jar, shake the oil and water, and let it stand. *What happens to the droplets? Can you tease them back together again?*

Now dip the toothpick into a jar of detergent, and then touch it to the center of the water in your jar, watching carefully as you do so. *What happens at the oil/water surface?*

Cover the jar; then shake the oil and water a few times. Hold the jar up to the light and observe the contents carefully, using a magnifier if one is available. *Are there more or fewer droplets of oil than before? Are they larger or smaller?* Add a tiny bit more detergent, shake the mixture, and observe it once more. *What change can you*

see in the number and size of the oil droplets? Also try other substances such as motor oil, kerosine, and butter.

Detergents and soaps help to break oil and grease into tiny droplets. When the droplets are small enough, they do not stick to hands and dishes, but wash away easily in water.

WISE
WATER USE

Children often hear about water shortages and may even be affected by them. As the population soars, water shortages will become more common, and obtaining sufficient water for daily needs will be an increasing problem. Since their generation will have to face the problem, pupils should appreciate how much water is used in daily living and learn to use it wisely. To help them do so, have each engage in a weekend or vacation-period cooperative venture to study his family's and community's use of water as follows:

First, stick a strip of waterproof adhesive tape vertically inside a clean plastic pail. Then *calibrate* the pail by filling it with water, a quart at a time, and making pencil marks on the tape to indicate quarts and gallons.

Next, remove the cover from a toilet tank and mark where the water level comes. Then close the shutoff valve in the pipe beneath the tank. Flush the toilet and refill the tank from the plastic pail, recording how much water it takes. Replace the cover, turn on the valve, and place a card and a pencil on the cover for members of the family to record each time they flush the toilet. Do this for each toilet if there is more than one in the house. *How much water is required to flush a toilet? How much is used by the family during one entire 24-hour day for this purpose?*

Put another strip of adhesive tape vertically on the inside of the bathtub, near the drain. When someone takes a bath, have him draw the water, a gallon at a time, in the calibrated pail, and pour it into the

tub, making a mark on the strip of tape for each gallon added. *How much is used, on an average, for a bath?*

To find out how much is used for a shower, stopper the tub before the water is turned on and let the water collect in the tub until the shower is finished. Then record the volume as indicated by the calibrated strip of adhesive tape. *Which takes more water, on an average, a shower or a bath? How does the volume compare with that needed to flush a toilet? How much water does the family use per day for bathing and showering?*

To measure the water used for such things as washing a car or watering a lawn, turn the hose or sprinkler into the calibrated pail and record the length of time to collect a gallon. *How much water does the hose or the sprinkler discharge per minute? Per hour?*

Also try to measure how much water is used for cooking, for washing dishes, and for similar daily tasks. If it is difficult to measure

the water used in a washing machine, check the book of instructions that came with the machine, or call the appliance dealer to see if he can supply the information.

To find out how much water the family has used in a single day, add together the amounts recorded for all uses, or read the water meter at the beginning and at the end of a day. It will indicate the water used in terms of cubic feet. (One cubic foot equals about 7 1/2 gallons.) *How much water is used by the family in one day?*

When each pupil has completed a record of how much water his family uses, let him add it to the records of the rest of the class. *How much water, on the average, does each pupil require for his own normal daily activities? How much, on the average, does each family represented require?*

Finally, let the class find out from one or more local industrial plants how much water they use each day, on an average. Then, by dividing this amount by the number of peo-

ple employed, pupils can determine the average daily water consumption per employee. *How does the industrial average per employee compare with the home-use average per person? What kinds of industries use the most water?*

The supply of fresh water available for human needs is limited. At the same time, the use of water for both home and industrial purposes is increasing. Hence, drastic reductions in its use or some cheaper ways of obtaining fresh water from sea water will be needed before many years if prolonged shortages and harmful consequences are to be avoided. Since the pupils of today will be the adults who will be faced with these problems, they should think about ways in which water can be conserved. *Where does water seem to be wasted at home? At school? In other ways in the community? What are some reasonable ways that the amount of water used could be decreased without affecting ordinary sanitation requirements?*

LADDER
FOR LIQUIDS

In "Holey Scow," water was observed to cling to itself, or *cohere*. However, many liquids, including water, also stick to other materials, or *adhere*. Depending upon their abilities both to cohere and to adhere, they often do interesting

things such as climb inside slender tubes, creep up or down the sides of containers, and soak into porous materials. Besides being useful in lamp and candle wicks, sponges, and soil, this climbing or *capillary action* provides an intriguing matter to investigate.

Let each pupil in a group cut a 10-inch strip from different materials such as cloth, paper towel, and corrugated cardboard, and tape one end of each to a ruler resting across two books standing on end. Then have each pupil fill a paper cup with water to which some food coloring has been added for visibility. At a signal let them all put their cups under their strips and observe how the water climbs. *In which strip does the water rise fastest? In which has it risen farthest after five minutes? After a half hour? What differences can be observed if kerosine is used in place of water? If salad oil is used? Rubbing alcohol?*

Now let each group compare, as follows, the rate at which water moves up, and then *down*, liquid ladders. Fill a cup with colored water and set it on another cup, which has been inverted. Cut several equal-size strips, as before, long enough for one end to dip into the full cup and the other end to dangle into an empty cup below. Make a point on the dangling end. Put the strips in place and watch what happens.

Through which of the strips does the water soak to the point? Does the water stop moving in a strip when it has soaked to the point? At the end of a half hour, what has happened in the empty cups? The full cups? What will happen if they are left overnight? What explanation can be offered for what is observed?

firsthand experiences

Firsthand experiences are, in the last analysis, the basis of learning. A person's education rests, fundamentally, upon his direct contacts with the world about him, through seeing, hearing, feeling, smelling, tasting, and other sensory channels.

Unfortunately, this truth seems all too often to be forgotten. So readily do we substitute books about things for the things themselves, films for field trips, telling for discovering, television for participation, and memorizing for investigating.

Of course, vicarious experiences—those which one has indirectly, through the medium of others—are often highly worthwhile. In fact, at times they may be the only feasible means of developing concepts. Certainly there is no question of the value of books, pictures, recordings, and other instructional aids. But they can never fully replace firsthand, direct experiences.

As an example, can reading about air pressure substitute for actually feeling it? (See "Air Push.") Does watching spots of light in a planetarium truly take the place of seeing real stars move across the sky? (See "Star Shifts.") Is listening to someone tell about the delay of echoes as effective as actually hearing and measuring this delay? (See "Sound Bounce.")

Can one really convey to a child, by words, the fragrance of mint, the flavor of wintergreen, or the sting of nettle? How adequate a concept of snow can a youngster have who has never seen snow, felt snow, eaten snow, or otherwise experienced snow?

The same point holds true for much of what is taught in school, be it about soil erosion, pond life, the seasons, water vapor, or the methods used by scientists. Firsthand experiences are needed to make such subjects more meaningful to pupils; this book suggests only a small sampling of the many that are possible.

powders
and
solutions

4

Many of the common materials in daily life—nylon, drugs, plastics, paper, inks and dyes, aluminum foil, rubber, and glass—are the result of chemistry. By chemical action, certain substances are refined and treated or are combined with other substances to produce products that are stronger than, more corrosion-resistant than, or otherwise superior to, products of the past. With some knowledge of chemistry, a person can appreciate these materials and understand certain chemical reactions that others can only take for granted.

Much of the early chemistry to which children are exposed is in the form of chemistry sets or chemistry magic in books. They are *told* about atoms and molecules; instead, they should *experience* common reactions. It is far better for them to face theory after they have observed some of the evidence; theory serves only to explain what is observed.

Elementary experiences with powders and solutions do not necessitate chemical glassware and bunsen burners. Ordinary containers and heat sources will suffice for investigations of most common chemicals. For substances such as table salt (sodium chloride), common names and chemical names should be used interchangeably. If activities are limited to common chemicals, children will be encouraged to repeat and extend their investigations at home.

Safety precautions, such as having a fire extinguisher and water source handy, should be stressed and small amounts of chemicals used for all investigations; but the need for precautions should not deter a teacher from teaching chemistry, any more than the need to observe traffic lights should keep him from crossing the street. The thrill of seeing things happen and of obtaining predictable results should make working with powders and solutions an enjoyable and valuable experience for both teachers and pupils.

SOME IMPORTANT OBJECTIVES

ATTITUDES AND APPRECIATIONS TO BE ENCOURAGED:

Chemical changes take place all around us, often unnoticed; they are not confined to test tubes, beakers, and flasks.

Substances are made and destroyed by chemical action, but the basic stuff of which they are made is neither created nor destroyed.

If two substances exhibit similar behavior in every way when tested, they are assumed to be the same.

All substances, even ordinary ones such as air, water, salt, paper, and concrete consist of chemicals.

Chemical changes are often predictable; therefore, chemists can plan for certain reactions and obtain the expected results.

Some chemical changes, such as fires and explosions, are rapid; others, such as corrosion and rusting, are slow. Either can be destructive or helpful, depending upon how it affects man.

Man is faced with a dilemma: by creating materials that do not corrode he produces longer-lasting refuse and litter.

Water and air contain increasing amounts of impurities harmful to man; these impurities result from chemical changes carried out by him.

Some chemicals are poisonous or otherwise dangerous; therefore it is essential, when experimenting, to follow directions, use only small amounts, label all containers, keep them where young children cannot get them, and have water handy for washing and for emergency.

To chemists we owe many modern products such as plastics, drugs, and synthetic fibers; more and better things are yet to come.

SKILLS AND HABITS TO BE DEVELOPED:

Measuring liquid volumes by using drops, by marking containers, etc.

Weighing solids quickly and accurately on pupil-made or commercial balances

Labeling containers and substances accurately and legibly

Pouring and mixing liquids safely, without spilling, splashing, or contamination

Dissolving materials rapidly and distinguishing undissolved from insoluble material

Testing water samples for small amounts of dissolved solids

Removing all traces of chemicals after investigations involving liquid or solid substances

Taking samples from more than one container of chemicals without contaminating the supplies

Heating liquids safely by using a hot plate or by lighting an alcohol-filled bottle cap set in a pie pan

Providing sufficient oxygen for a purposeful flame and efficiently limiting the oxygen supply to an unwanted flame

Using correctly terms such as chemical change, dissolve, solution, residue, dilution, oxygen, carbon dioxide, crystal, corrode, ignite, extinguish, and react

FACTS AND PRINCIPLES TO BE TAUGHT:

Air (because of the oxygen in it) is necessary for ordinary burning and rusting.

Salt and other solids may be obtained by evaporation of sea water.

A flame may be extinguished by surrounding it with a substance that does not burn and that keeps air from getting to the flame.

Some substances are corroded by water, air, vinegar, and other chemicals, and the rate of corrosion depends upon both the chemicals and the temperature.

Sea water contains chemicals washed into it from air and from land.

Solid materials coming out of solution often are in crystalline form.

Gases dissolve more easily in cold liquids than in warm ones, but solids usually dissolve more readily in warm liquids.

Substances differ in the ease with which they dissolve.

Crystals that grow without interference have definite shapes, with flat faces that meet at definite angles.

Some chemical changes take place rapidly and even violently, most are not so rapid, and some are extremely slow.

Some materials are extremely resistant to chemical change.

During the process of chemical change, substances with certain characteristics are changed into other substances with different characteristics.

CANDLE QUENCHER

Carbon dioxide is an interesting and useful gas easily made from a common powder and a familiar solution. It does not burn or explode, and is not poisonous. Pupils should get to know it!

To make some, put a heaping teaspoonful of baking soda (sodium bicarbonate) in a pint jar, pour in a quarter cup of vinegar, and quickly cover the mouth of the jar with a flat, close-fitting piece of cardboard.

Caution: Do not screw or clamp a lid on the jar!

Next, stand a candle in a lump of modeling clay in a pie pan, and light it. Then, after the foaming in the jar has stopped, take the cardboard off and pour the contents of the jar—*but not the liquid contents*—on the flame, from above it and a short distance away. *What happens? Can anyone see why?*

Let pupils try this, too, under close supervision. Everyone should have a turn, but there should be only one candle or a few, each guarded by a pupil.

Caution: He should have a can of water at hand!

The vinegar and soda act together chemically to form carbon dioxide. When poured on a flame, this gas pushes the air away, and the fire goes out. Many fire extinguishers direct carbon dioxide at fires; others use it to make water or foam squirt out.

Later, as a follow-up to this experience, pupils may:

1. Ask a custodian to demonstrate a carbon dioxide extinguisher, and perhaps other kinds as well, on a small fire made outdoors.

2. Pour a little vinegar in a plastic bag, add some baking soda, and squeeze the mouth of the bag shut. *What happens?*

3. Open two large paper bags and hang them by single threads from the ends of a long, thin stick suspended by a thread tied to its middle. Adjust the threads until the stick hangs level. Then pour a gallon jarful of carbon dioxide into one of the bags. *What does it do? Why?*

FLAME LIFE EXPECTANCY

A candle needs air to burn; this fact is neatly shown by covering the candle with a jar. Further, the life of the flame varies when jars of assorted sizes and shapes are used. *Why does this happen?*

Have all the pupils bring jars, which should range in size from a quart to the smallest anyone can find. Then divide the class into groups, each having a birthday-cake candle standing in a lump of modeling clay on a smooth desk top. Appoint a "Candlekeeper" for each candle; he should be responsible for lighting it properly.

Caution: He should have a can of water at hand!

Also let one pupil serve as "Timekeeper" for the class. He is to say "Ready. Set. Go!" and at "Go!" release a "Swinging Second-timer" and count its swings aloud.

Now let each pupil, in turn, set his jar over the lighted candle at the word "Go!" *How long does it burn?* Have him record this. Then let him measure the volume of the jar by filling it with water from a measuring cup. Each pupil should repeat both measurements at least once, after fanning fresh air into the jar.

Rule a grid on the chalkboard, with evenly spaced vertical lines labeled in seconds, by 10's, from 0 to 120; and horizontal lines marked in fluid ounces, by 10's, up to 140. Then let the pupils make x's on the grid to indicate the volume of each jar and how long the candle burned in it. When all have done this, draw a smooth line through as many x's as possible, so that about as many of those it misses are on one side as on the other. This line shows the relation between the volume of air and the flame life.

According to this graph, how long should a candle flame "live" in a 2-quart jar? In a gallon jar? Extend the line until it crosses the lines that indicate the measured volumes of these jars. Are these predictions confirmed by actual tests? If not, what other factors may be involved? How could one check to see?

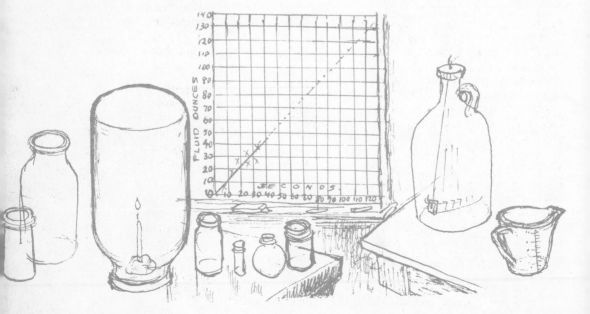

SUPER SOLUTION

There is more of one liquid solution in the world than of any other—more, in fact, than of *all* other solutions put together!

Who can tell what it is? If pupils are baffled, give them a few clues, one at a time, such as: It has an unforgettable taste! Fish can live in it! Most of the earth is covered by it!

Many children do not appreciate what sea water is like, yet they often read about the sea. Therefore, it may be worthwhile to let a class write to another class of the same grade in some coastal village, requesting a pint or two of *clean* sea water in exchange for an interesting plant, mineral, fossil, or other specimen. They should suggest mailing the water in a *plastic* bottle with a screw cap, packed well in newspaper in a strong carton.

When the sea water arrives, distribute it to small groups of pupils so that they can:

1. Put some in a jar, set the jar in a pan of water, and boil the water for 20 minutes. After letting it cool, taste the sterilized sample.

2. Let a little evaporate in a small glass dish, and examine the residue with a magnifier. *Are there any crystals?* Then add more sea water from time to time. (See "Reappearing Act.")

3. Try making soapsuds with sea water. Then dissolve some table salt in *rain water* and test it with soap. *Does the sea water seem to contain more than just table salt?*

4. Leave a nail in sea water and another nail in tap water. *Which rusts faster?* Try other iron objects and some of copper and brass. *How do they compare? Of what practical importance is this?*

5. Mix a little mud in sea water and an equal amount in some rain water. *In which do the finest particles settle quicker?* Also try this with creek water. *How might this process affect what occurs when a river flows into the sea?*

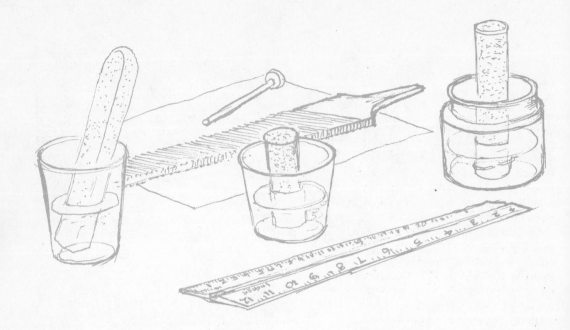

INVISIBLE
SOLUTION

In "Super Solution," pupils are asked to name the most abundant liquid solution in the world. There is even more of another solution, not a liquid. It is air, a solution of gases.

Pupils can easily obtain evidence of two different gases in air. Ask each to bring a small, slender bottle, vial, toothbrush tube, or similar container, and also a jar in which this container can be inverted. Then have them, in small groups or at odd times, rub large nails on flat files to make iron powder. Next, let each wet the inside of his container, add a large pinch of the iron powder so that it sticks to the sides, and set the container, mouth down, in an inch of water in the jar.

Why does the water not rise higher in the containers? How could one tell if some of the enclosed air were removed?

Let the class observe the containers for several days. *What hap-pens to the water levels? What does this suggest? Does the water, in time, fill the containers, or does it rise only so far?*

Meanwhile, what happens to the iron powder? Is there any sign of a new substance being formed? Does all the iron change, or is some left unchanged? How might a magnet be used to check this?

After a few days, ask each pupil to estimate or measure what fraction of the volume of his container has filled with water and to write this on the chalkboard. *Is there any general agreement? Does the amount of iron seem to make any difference, as long as some is left unrusted? What if no iron is used? Might any other factors affect the water levels?* (See "Bottle Baro-scope.")

In rusting, the iron combines with part of the air and removes it; this is the gas named *oxygen.* The gas that is left does not affect the iron; this is nearly all *nitrogen. According to the class's findings, about how much of air is oxygen? Nitrogen?*

ONE
IN A MILLION

What does it mean to rinse out a glass? How much of what was in a glass remains, even after rinsing? If each pupil follows these directions, he will appreciate that rinsing is really *diluting*—often to one in a million, or even more.

Using a medicine dropper, put 99 drops of water in a paper cup. Then add one drop of food coloring. Remove the rubber bulb from the dropper and let water run through and over the glass tube to wash away all traces of coloring. Replace the bulb and stir the mixture in the cup. The cup now contains 100 drops of liquid, of which one is food coloring. This ratio of 1:100 is the *dilution* of the food coloring.

Put a drop of this mixture into a second cup, add 99 drops of water, and stir it. Now the dilution is 1 in 100 *in* 100, or 1 in 10,000. Put a drop of this mixture into a third cup, add 99 drops of water, and stir. The dilution in this third cup is 1 in a million (1/100 of 1/100 of 1/100). Put 100 drops of water in a fourth cup and compare the appearance of water with that of the diluted food coloring in the third cup. *Can you see any difference?* But you *know* there is food coloring in one because you *put* it there!

Pour out the contents of the third cup. *Do the one or two drops remaining in it contain any food coloring?* Imagine how dilute the coloring would be if you filled the cup with water again before emptying it!

To supplement the pupils' investigation, prepare cups of lemon juice and maple syrup, diluted 1:10, 1:100, and so on. Put a dropper in

each cup for dropping the solutions on pupils' tongues. Then blindfold a pupil at a time and test him with various dilutions. *What is the most dilute solution he can identify in three out of four tries? Is there any common extract or flavoring that can be identified correctly when diluted to one part in a million?*

BUBBLES
FROM NOWHERE

Most pupils know that there is gas in soda pop; they have seen the bubbles and felt the fizz. However, they may not know that water often contains gas, too, which comes out under certain conditions. Working alone or in small groups, each with two glass tumblers, a test tube, a bottle of clear pop such as ginger ale or 7-Up, a hand magnifier, and a thermometer, they can investigate gas leaving a solution, as follows:

Fill both tumblers with cold water and record its temperature. Label each glass with this temperature and the names of the pupils in the group, leaving one glass in the room ·at a place where it will not be disturbed and placing the other in a refrigerator. After an hour, examine the glass in the room. *Can you see any bubbles in it?* Take the temperature of the water. *How does it compare with the original?*

Now examine the glass in the refrigerator. *Are there bubbles in it? How do they compare with those in the other glass? How does the temperature of this water compare with the other?*

Let the pupils propose explanations for what they see, and on this basis let them try predicting what will happen if the glasses are filled with warm water instead of cold at the start. Then let them try it. *How do the* observed *results compare with the* predicted results? Let them try, also, glasses of cold and warm water in sunlight and in shade. *Does the light make a difference, or does sunlight merely warm the water and thus cause bubbles to form? Can you think of a way to test your ideas?*

Have each group fill its test tube completely full with cold tap water. Then have one pupil put a fingertip in the mouth of the test tube and lever it upward to reduce

the pressure inside. *Do any air bubbles form and rise?* Let the water stand until it is about room temperature. *Do more bubbles form?*

Tap water, like soda pop, is under pressure until it is released from its container, the pipe. Some of the air dissolved in it comes out —partly, perhaps, because the pressure is reduced, but chiefly because the water warms. Warm water cannot contain as much dissolved gas as cold water. Bubbles can be seen forming in water heating on a stove, before the water has begun to boil. The bubbles may be air, or they may be water vapor (steam). *Can anyone think of a way to collect some of the bubbles and then test them to find out?* When a group has an idea, let them try it (with supervision, of course) for the rest of the class.

Soda pop is a solution of carbon dioxide in water, but since it is dissolved under pressure, much of

it escapes when the pressure is reduced. Like air bubbles in water, carbon dioxide bubbles in pop seem to come from nowhere as the gas leaves its solution.

Let the pupils, working in small groups, investigate bubbles in pop as follows: Carefully remove the cap from a bottle of clear pop at room temperature. *What can you see happening in the liquid?* Let someone put his mouth over the opening of the upright bottle and force air into it as hard as he can while the rest check the bubbling rate. Then let him try to suck air from the bottle. *How does this affect the bubbling rate?*

Pour some pop into a glass and look carefully through a magnifier at where the bubbles form. *Do they form just anywhere, or do they seem to form more readily on the surface of the glass itself? Do any form one after another at a particular spot? Do they appear suddenly as large bubbles, or do they grow* *from nothing to one big enough to break free and float to the top? What happens if you hit the glass with a pencil?*

Some other activities for pupils to try when investigating bubbles from nowhere are:

1. Stick a finger in a glass of soda pop and compare the formation of bubbles on it with that on the glass itself.

2. Stick a small piece of adhesive tape to the bottom of a glass, pour pop in the glass, and see where bubbles form most readily.

3. Drop a few grains of salt into a glass of pop. *How do they affect bubble formation? Do sand grains do the same?*

4. Put some pop in a test tube and then reduce the pressure on it in the same way as with tap water and check the effect on bubble formation.

REAPPEARING ACT

Most pupils have seen sugar and salt dissolve and apparently disappear in water, but probably few have investigated to see what happens to these substances when the water evaporates. *Do they evaporate, too, or are they left behind? If left behind, are they changed to something else?* Some simple activities will tell.

Set out some labeled dishes of common chemicals such as salt, sugar, baking soda, alum, and epsom salt, with a plastic spoon in each. For each group of five pupils provide five paper cups, a medicine dropper, a magnifier, a sheet of dark paper, and a small, clean pane of window glass. Then let each group proceed as follows:

Put a half-teaspoonful of salt in one of the cups. Dump a few grains onto the dark paper and examine them carefully with the magnifier. *What shape do they have? What do they taste like?*

On the pane of glass, label as many spots as there are chemicals to be tested. Set the glass hori-

zontally in a warm place. Next, add a teaspoonful of water to the salt in the cup, stir with the medicine dropper until it dissolves completely, and then make a puddle of a few drops near the proper label on the glass. Rinse the dropper, and repeat the process with the other chemicals.

(*Note:* These chemicals are harmless to taste in small amounts.)

In the morning, check to see if any drops have left a *residue. Does any of the residue resemble the original substance?* Test each for taste. *Which tastes like the original?* Watch through a magnifier as you add a drop of vinegar to the residue from baking soda. *Does anything happen like what you saw in "Candle Quencher"?*

Many chemicals that seem to disappear in water reappear when the water evaporates. Some examples are spots on windows and on glasses that are not wiped dry. Residues that accumulate over a long period of time in caverns and tunnels or under concrete bridges may leave hard projections such as stalactites and stalagmites.

planned programs

Although firsthand experiences, supplemented by vicarious ones, are basic to good science teaching, these experiences can hardly occur in a haphazard, unrelated fashion. They need to be part of a planned program. For one thing, a teacher should be able to expect that in the previous grades his class has had certain experiences and has attained certain goals on which he can build.

To present such a program is not a purpose of this book. Many good programs are already available—in textbook series, state courses of study, and curriculum guides developed by committees of teachers. Some of these programs are outstanding in that they:

1. Have clear and worthwhile objectives—including ones that deal with attitudes, appreciations, and skills, in addition to the usual ones involving knowledge—together with numerous practical suggestions for helping pupils attain these objectives

2. Are sequential, suggesting simple skills and ideas to be developed in the lower grades in accordance with the ability and interest of the children and gradually introducing more complex processes and materials as the pupils grow in maturity and experience

3. Deal with content that is well suited to children instead of crowding down into the grades material from high school and college courses—including highly abstract concepts which have no place in the elementary school.

4. Include a good balance of material drawn from the physical, biological, and earth sciences, with no major gaps or pointless repetition, and so coordinated with the entire instructional program that science is not isolated from other subjects

5. Require ample time for science—just as for reading, social studies, and mathematics—to permit a wealth of experiences, coupled with reflection, discussion, and fun

rocks and the land

5

Children are fascinated by rocks, minerals, and fossils, and bring them to school at the slightest encouragement. They are intrigued, also, by canyons, mountains, and waterfalls. Their interest in these things is good, and should be nourished.

After all, man depends on earth materials and features for a great many of his needs—stone for buildings, soil for crops, petroleum for fuel, valleys for reservoirs, and hills for recreation, to mention only a few. How wisely he acts in using these materials and in changing these features is of major importance to his well-being. Thus, it is essential that he have a sound understanding of rocks and the land.

A person's conception of the earth—its composition, the changes occurring on it and within it, and its long history—is based, in the last analysis, on his firsthand experiences. Many of these experiences stem from commonplace things—including mud puddles, gullied lawns, broken sidewalks, and other miniature counterparts of major geological features. Such experiences are highly worthwhile. Interesting and informative in themselves, they also furnish a foundation for comprehending abstract and complex concepts about the earth—how seas flood the lands, why there are canyons, what causes earthquakes, and the like.

What is taught in this area should depend—perhaps to a greater degree than in other areas—on what there is nearby. This will, of course, vary from place to place, but certainly there is *some* geology to be observed at first hand *wherever* one happens to be! It is better to let children explore the rocks, soils, and landforms with which they can have direct experiences than to have them learn mostly about faraway and spectacular features with which their experiences can only be vicarious.

SOME IMPORTANT OBJECTIVES

ATTITUDES AND APPRECIATIONS TO BE ENCOURAGED:

Rocks and the land are interesting, and become even more so as we observe them and learn more about them.

Man learns about earth materials and processes through observation, testing, measurement, and experimentation.

In learning about the earth we should base our ideas on sound evidence and arrive at conclusions and inferences cautiously.

Although man knows a great deal concerning the earth and its history, there is a great deal more to be learned.

Earth features and events result from natural processes; they can be explained without resorting to supernatural causes.

Man's knowledge of the earth's past is inference, based on incomplete information gathered from rocks, fossils, and landscapes.

Some of the changes which man is increasingly able to make in the landscape have, or may have, undesirable consequences.

It is important that man use rocks, minerals, and soils wisely, for his own well-being now and in the future.

SKILLS AND HABITS TO BE DEVELOPED:

Observing differences in the shape, smoothness, color, clarity, and composition of pebbles, sand grains, and other stones

Noticing that some rocks are being, or have been, broken, worn, discolored, and decomposed by natural processes

Classifying stones as angular or rounded, and as boulders, cobbles, pebbles, granules, sand, silt, and clay

Detecting places where soil and loose rock are being, or have been, eroded and deposited and estimating to what extent

Recognizing layers of sediment and sedimentary rock that were probably deposited in water

Telling the order of deposition of undisturbed layers of sediment or sedimentary rock

Determining whether rocks have tiny pore spaces within them

Measuring the volume of pore space in sand and gravel

Distinguishing between rocks which consist of interlocking mineral grains and those composed of particles stuck together

Labeling samples of rocks and soils accurately and clearly

Using correctly such terms as abrasion, bedrock, canyon, erosion, fossil, geologist, mineral, pore, sediment, and sorting

FACTS AND PRINCIPLES TO BE TAUGHT:

The surface of the land is shaped by gravity, water, air, ice, and living things, but chiefly by water working because of, and with, gravity.

▬ In nature rocks often become broken, worn, and decomposed—some more readily than others—forming smaller and smaller pieces.

▬ Rain, streams, and waves move and deposit soil and loose pieces of rock and usually sort them according to particle size.

▬ Some rocks consist of pieces of older rocks which have become cemented or compressed so that they stick together.

▬ The particles in many rocks do not fit together closely; the spaces between them often contain water and sometimes oil and gas.

▬ Some rocks contain fossils—the remains and other evidences of ancient plants and animals.

▬ Some rocks consist of interlocked grains of minerals, probably formed under great pressure or as molten material cooled, or as a result of a combination of both.

- Although earth materials and features are continually being changed, the same materials are often used again and again.

- Earth processes that occurred in the past seem, in general, to have been similar to those which are taking place today.

- Earth processes are usually slow, and yet their effects are often great; therefore it is apparent that they have been going on for a very long time.

PEBBLE JAR

In many areas there is an interesting variety of pebbles. Pupils should become familiar with them as an early step in learning about rocks. This they can do by making a pebble jar.

Find a tall, plain jar. Ask each pupil to bring in a colorful or otherwise interesting pebble, wash it well, and carefully place it in the jar. If there is still room, let those whose pebbles cannot easily be seen add others, until the jar is full. Then, while the class watches, fill the jar with water. *Does the water seem to change the size of the pebbles?* (See "Big Finger.") Stand the jar near a window where pupils can examine the pebbles in good light, and have a magnifier handy.

Do the pebbles all look alike? Are they similar in shape and smoothness? What colors do they show? Do some have several colors? Do any shine or sparkle? Can light shine through some?

At this stage it is not important to tell the names of the rocks in the pebbles. However, pupils may wish to make up names which seem appropriate, such as black-and-white-stone, glass-stone, ribbon-stone, yellow-stone, and sparkle-stone.

If the pebbles were broken into tiny pieces about the size of sand grains, how many different kinds of grains would there be in all? Which color would be the most common?

Break up a few of the pebbles by wrapping one at a time in a plastic bag, placing it on a large rock or curbstone, and hitting it squarely with a hammer. Let the pupils look at the grains with a strong magnifier and also shake some in a jar of water.

Then let each pupil examine a pinch of clean sand with a magnifier. *Are there grains of different colors in it? Do they look like tiny pieces of broken rock? Might rocks get broken into sand naturally? If so, where and how could this happen?*

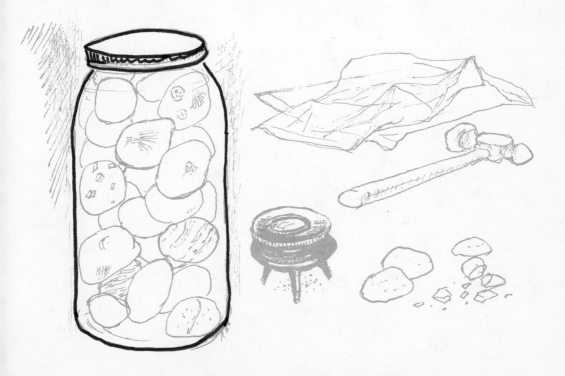

MUDPILE MOUNTAIN

It is interesting that some of the same principles involved in the shaping of mountains also apply to the erosion of mudpiles. This makes it easy for pupils, even in flat country, to get a better understanding of mountains—and quickly, too!

To start, ask each pupil to rule lines 1 centimeter apart across both sides of a few "popsicle" sticks or tongue depressors, starting at one end. Then have them crayon centimeter-wide bands, neatly, in this order: red, green, orange, blue, yellow, purple.

Next, take the class out to a patch of bare ground, and dig up earth without pebbles or larger stones. Dump it in a pile and tamp it down to make a "mountain" about half a meter high. Now let the pupils push their sticks into the "mountain" and the surrounding "land," red ends out, so that they are at right angles to the surface and evenly distributed. The boundary between the orange and blue bands should be even with the surface.

Then help the pupils sprinkle the "mountain" with a watering can or a garden hose propped up so that the "rain" falls straight down. *Do the markers indicate erosion to be taking place? Where? Are some places being built up? Does a real rain cause any changes?*

Let the class continue to erode the "mountain" and observe it for several days. *Which of these features are formed in miniature: streams (S), canyons (C), waterfalls, lakes (L), deltas (D), landslides, alluvial fans (F)? Which is carried farther by the water, sand or silt? Silt or clay?* (See "Sorted Stones.") *What, if anything, on the "mountain" seems to retard the erosion?*

Caution pupils not to carry this comparison too far. Mountains are not just big piles of earth but consist chiefly of bedrock, and this is not simply washed away. Further, there is the matter of scale: On a mudpile "mountain" a sand grain is a boulder!

BRICK
PEBBLES

Too often pupils read and talk about how water wears away rocks without having any experiences with what really happens. Yet a class can easily learn at first hand how the abrasion of rocks may occur by making some brick "pebbles" as a project.

Break a common "soft" red brick with a hammer. Put 6 to 10 *angular* pieces, each about an inch across, in a strong, thick-walled jar with a cover. Add water until the jar is half full, close it tightly, and place it in a paper bag in case it should crack.

Ask 10 pupils to give the jar 100 shakes each—not so hard as to break the glass. Then let the class examine the fragments, observe the color of the water, and scrape the inside of the jar with their fingernails. Pour the water into a gallon jar, and let the mud settle. (See "Sorted Stones.")

Let pupils repeat this, giving the

fragments 1,000 shakes each day until they are well rounded. Have them record the number of shakes, note changes in the fragments and the jar, and save the mud. *Does the water abrade the fragments, or do they wear each other and the jar? Where does this sort of thing happen to real rocks? Might mud be formed from these rocks?*

A record of the pebble-rounding may be made with an overhead projector. The angular fragments are crayoned heavily on one side, placed on the projector with this side down, and projected on paper taped to the wall. Their silhouettes are traced exactly and then cut out. A new set of cutouts is made after each 1,000 shakes, always with the fragments in the same position and the projector at the same distance from the paper. The cutouts are then mounted to show the change in shape of the "pebbles."

Can rocks like sandstone or limestone also be abraded in this way? Does sand speed up the process? Let pupils find out!

LOST SOIL

Water from rain and melting snow carries soil and loose rock material with it as it runs downhill to streams, lakes, and the sea. In this way much valuable topsoil is lost. Although this loss cannot be stopped entirely, it is important that we do everything we can to reduce it.

Pupils can learn at first hand about soil erosion and ways to retard it by making a few *controlled* experiments. In each of these there are two setups, alike except for *one* factor. This is the factor which the experiment is designed to test. The basic experiment is described first, followed by several modifications of it. In each case, two miniature "fields," different in one respect, are sprinkled, and the amount of erosion is compared.

1. Get two identical rectangular pans, such as aluminum cake pans. Fill them with soil, preferably sandy. Pack it down, and level it off even with the top edge. Set the pans out-doors on a clean concrete walk. Leave one flat, and tilt the other by propping up one end on a brick or block. Then sprinkle them *equally* with a watering can or garden hose, or wait for a heavy rain. *How do the level and sloping surfaces compare with respect to the amount of soil washed out onto the concrete?*

2. Tilt *both* pans of soil, one steeply and the other gently.

3. Fill one pan with sod "scalped" from a mowed lawn, or plant the soil in it with grass, radishes, or oats. Leave the soil in the other pan bare, and tilt both pans an equal amount.

4. Tilt both pans equally, and "plow" the soil in them with a stick so that the miniature furrows run up and down one slope, and across the other to represent *contour plowing.*

5. Mulch the soil in one pan with dead leaves or straw, and leave the soil bare in the other. Tilt both pans the same amount.

STONE SIZES

Pieces of rock, or stones, show a great range in size. Pupils can become aware of this and learn the conventional names for the various sizes by collecting many stones and sorting them.

Ask each pupil to gather three stones of different sizes. Then, possibly outdoors, have the class line up all their stones in a row, from largest to smallest. Let them fill any big gaps with the sizes that are missing. *Should tiny pebbles be included? How about sand grains—are they also pieces of rock?*

Next, have them put labels on the various sizes, as follows:

Boulders (more than 256 millimeters across)

Cobbles (64 to 256 millimeters across)

Pebbles (4 to 64 millimeters across)

Granules (2 to 4 millimeters across)

Sand (1/16 to 2 millimeters across)

Can you find, and add to the collection, any pieces of rock that are even smaller than sand grains? These are the particles in *silt* and *clay*. Samples may be obtained from dried-up mud puddles and placed in small jars or in plastic bags or boxes.

Silt is about as fine as scouring powder. It rubs off easily and crumbles readily when dry. If a little is rubbed between a coin and a can held up to one's ear, it makes a grinding sound. For comparison, the coin and can should be tried alone, first.

Clay consists of rock particles so tiny that they cannot be seen without a microscope. Their small size makes the clay feel very smooth. They stick together when moist, allowing the clay to be molded into shape, and they stay stuck together when dry.

Labeled samples of various sizes of stones may be kept, and referred to when examining the soil dug from a hole to plant a tree or reading about the Mississippi Delta.

BOULDERS COBBLES PEBBLES GRANULES SAND SILT CLAY

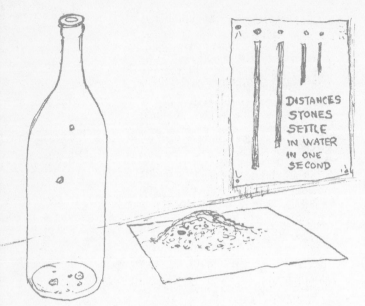

SORTED
STONES

As a follow-up to "Stone Sizes," pupils can investigate the sorting of stones, according to size, by water —a most important geological process. They can:

1. Fill a tall bottle with water. Drop in, at the same instant, a small pebble and a sand grain. Do this several times. *Which settles faster?* Now try a granule and a sand grain, sticking them to a wet fingertip and touching the water. Likewise, compare the settling of sand and silt. Finally, stir a little clay in water, let it stand, and note its settling.

2. Get some earth—without leaves, twigs, or roots—from beneath the topsoil in a road cut or excavation. Drop a handful into a tall jar nearly full of water, and watch it settle. *Does any sorting take place?* Add some more after a while, and later, still more. *What happens? Might the layers that are often seen in* sand and gravel banks have been deposited in water that existed there at one time? If so, which layer is oldest?

3. Dig up samples of earth from various places, and water-sort them to see if they are different. To make fair comparisons, put equal amounts in similar jars and add like volumes of water; then cover the jars tightly, shake them equally, and let them stand. *What differences show up? Do any of the samples consist of rock particles which are nearly all of similar size?*

4. Compare various samples of soil from gardens and fields by shaking them in water and letting them settle. Note the sizes of rock particles which the soils contain and also the organic matter, most of which settles only slowly or floats.

5. Use a "Swinging Second-timer" to measure how far tiny pebbles, granules, sand grains, and silt particles settle in water in one second.

YOUNG FOSSILS

Fossils seem to have a special appeal for children. They like to hunt for them, and often bring some to school. But even if none are found nearby, pupils can acquire a better understanding of what they are and how they may have been formed by making some "fossils" and "discovering" them.

First have them nearly fill a large pan with mud from a dried-up puddle. Let them add water to it gradually and take turns in stirring it with a stick until it is as smooth as pancake batter. This mud represents sediment deposited on the bottom of the sea. *What, in the sea, might stir up sediment?*

Next, while they are stirring the mud, let pupils take turns in dropping in shells, fish bones, crab claws, bits of coral, starfish, and other objects from the sea. Everyone should add something. *Does anything like this happen in the sea? How?*

Then set the pan aside and allow the mud to dry out. This takes less time in a heated room. The mud, when hard, is somewhat like the rocks formed when sea sediment hardens.

When the mud is completely dry, let each pupil have a hand in breaking it apart and discovering the "fossils" in the "rock." *Are the impressions of shells and bones in rock considered to be fossils, or must the actual remains of animals be present?*

In similar fashion, pupils may also make "fossils" like those that could be formed in a lake, using shells of freshwater clams and snails, crayfish claws, fish and bird bones, and leaves.

As a follow-up, it is worth taking a field trip to a nearby lake or seashore, or even a puddle, to see how fossils may be formed if conditions are suitable. *How much chance does a dead fish, twig, or insect have of becoming a fossil? What would have to happen to it? What usually does happen to it?*

SAND
SPACE

From past experience, perhaps with a "Pebble Jar," pupils may realize that stones do not fit together exactly but have gaps between them. Let them think about and investigate these gaps. *Are they separate, or do they all connect together? About how much space is there in a jarful of gravel?*

Fill a jar with clean, dry pebbles —from a beach, creek bed, or gravel bank—and then ask for estimates of the amount of space betwen them. *Is it one-half of a jarful, one-third, one-tenth, or what?* Have each pupil write down what he thinks.

Then let the pupils see how nearly right they are. To measure the amount of space, hold the pebbles tightly in the jar, turn it over, and lower it straight down into a bucket or deep pan of water. Now let the pebbles fall out gradually so that the air between them

stays in the jar. Mark the volume of air by a rubber band around the jar, placed at the water level while the jar is held so the inside and outside water levels are even. Then lift the jar out, and fill it with water up to the rubber band. This water is equal in volume to the space in the jarful of gravel. It may be measured with a 1-fluid-ounce paper cup or a measuring cup.

Another way to measure the space in gravel is to find how much water it takes to fill the jar to the brim when it is "full" of dry pebbles. Any trapped air bubbles must be shaken out. Let pupils try both methods, each several times, and record their findings. *Are the results the same each time?*

Does the jar contain the same amount of space when filled with different samples of gravel? How about smaller pebbles? Large pebbles with very small ones, or sand, between them? Pebbles that are much more round? Crushed stone from a driveway? Do marbles have

more space between them than pebbles, or less?

After having these experiences, it is worthwhile for pupils to investigate the space in sand. Sand space, as well as that in gravel, is far more important than many people realize —but first let pupils discover how much there is of it!

Is there more space in a quart of dry sand or in a quart of dry pebbles? Let pupils find this out by actual measurement, using both of the methods suggested above.

A third way to measure sand space is as follows: Use a 1-fluid-ounce paper cup to measure 8 cupfuls of water into a quart jar. Then add *dry* sand to the water, one level cupful at a time. Count them. Keep tapping the jar and adding sand. When the level surface of the wet sand just meets the top of the water, all the sand space is filled with water, and there is no extra water. *How much space, then, was there in this sand? What was the volume of the dry sand?*

The amount of space in sand or gravel may be expressed as a fraction, such as 8/34 (8 fluid ounces of space in 34 fluid ounces of sand), or in percent, such as 23.5 percent (8 fluid ounces divided by 34 fluid ounces and multiplied by 100). Incidentally, a quart contains 32 fluid ounces, but many "quart" jars hold more than this. (See "Quarts and Quasi-quarts.") Therefore, the actual volume of the jar must be measured.

As stated above, space in sand and gravel is very important. Water from rain and snow soaks into it, and deep underground this space is usually completely filled with water. Many wells get their water from such water-saturated sand or gravel.

Often sand has been cemented by minerals to form "solid" *sandstone* and, similarly, gravel has been cemented into the rock called *conglomerate*. Even so, there usually is much space left in them. This is why these rocks can hold huge amounts of water and, in places, natural gas and petroleum. Pupils can appreciate this better if they let drops of water soak into pieces of sandstone and conglomerate and count them, or if they weigh the pieces before and after soaking them. The concept is made even clearer by a three-dimensional model that represents much-magnified sandstone. To make it, fill a wooden berry basket with fairly large pebbles. Then drip diluted glue on them until they are all coated with it and the excess runs off. Let the glue dry, and break off the basket. The pebbles are then held together by glue in much the same way as the sand grains in sandstone are cemented by minerals. *Are the spaces between them all connected? Can pipe cleaners, threads, or pieces of wire be run through them?*

MINERALS IN MEMORIALS

An excellent way for pupils to observe the minerals that make up some rocks is to examine memorials in a cemetery or monument works, or polished stones in a building. It is best to get permission beforehand. Magnifying glasses, ideally a number of them, are most useful.

A colorful, coarse-grained stone is best to start with. *How many different colors are in it? Are some grains transparent like glass, others translucent like wax, and others opaque like tar? Do any shine like metal or show peacock-like colors?* As a rule, grains which look distinctly different are different minerals.

Which mineral is the most abundant? Are any rather rare? Could a flea walk across the stone on grains of just one kind, or would it have to hop to get from one of these to the next?

Do the grains fit tightly, or are there gaps between them? Let pupils drip water on them to see. *Does it seem more likely that the grains were once separate pieces of rock, like pebbles or sand grains, which became cemented together, or that they grew in place, like sugar crystals?* (See "Sand Space" and "Reappearing Act.")

Let pupils compare the minerals in stones of different kinds. *Are any alike? Are the various kinds distributed evenly, or are they bunched up in places? Do they form swirls, suggesting movement?*

Geologists infer that granite and other rocks often used for memorials were formed deep underground beneath *miles* of overlying rock, under tremendous pressure. *(How many memorials in a pile a mile high? What about the pressure under them?)* Here the rocks were hot, some of them liquid or semiliquid, and as they cooled, crystals of various minerals were formed. Such rocks are now seen at the earth's surface only because the great thickness of rock that was once above them has been eroded.

means of motivating

Probably the greatest "secret" of a good teacher is the ability to get children to want to learn. Properly motivated pupils learn without being coerced because, for them, learning is rewarding.

This is not to say that learning need not involve hard work. However, even vigorous activity is fun if it is satisfying. Think of the physical exertion during a ball game and the mental effort in solving a puzzle or playing checkers!

Pupils become motivated when they participate in activities which are rewarding to them. The rewards, however, must be immediate, or nearly so; long-range goals have little meaning for children in the grades. The teacher, nonetheless, must keep the ultimate aims in view, realizing that they can be attained, in part, by having pupils do things intriguing to them, such as:

1. Engaging in physical activities, particularly those involving large muscles (See "Broomstick Pulleys.")

2. Seeing, hearing, or otherwise sensing aesthetically pleasing things (See "Pebble Jar" and "Shingle Songs.")

3. Watching things move, especially with rapid or repeated motion (See "Reaction Carts" and "Fishless Aquariums.")

4. Being surprised or fooled by unusual or unexpected happenings (See "Air Push" and "Big Finger.")

5. Competing with one another when everyone has a good chance of success (See "Ice-melting Contest.")

6. Making estimates and predictions, and then seeing how nearly right they are (See "Shadow Stick.")

7. Solving puzzles and problems—primarily physical ones, as well as mental ones (See "Super Solution" and "Night Lights.")

8. Exercising control over phenomena—making things work (See "Diving Dropper" and "Needle Poles.")

plants
and
animals

6

The interest of young children in plants and animals is obvious. Their squeals of delight when playing with pets; their frequent imitations of animal sounds; and their irresistible urge to pick a pretty, fragrant flower—all these attest to their fascination with living things. Properly nurtured, this interest can continue through life, broadening to include all sorts of animals, and plants that have no flowers at all.

Plants and animals can be studied at any season, indoors or out. Even in the "dead" of winter, trees are very much alive. So are seeds on weed stems and in packets, creatures in ponds, and spiders in cellars. The pupils themselves—the most important animals of all—are always available for study.

To study plants and animals requires little more than keen eyes and an inquisitive nature. Magnifiers and microscopes are helpful but not necessary. Materials are free or inexpensive, and plants and animals exist in some form wherever a school is located.

Pupils can experiment freely with plants and not feel that they are hurting them. However, experiments that may cause injury or distress to animals should be discouraged. There is plenty to do and to observe without risking an animal's well-being. Also, if native animals are used, they can be released when interest in them wanes; exotic animals cannot be released without possible harm to them or to our native species.

The lessons learned from plants and animals are basic to conservation attitudes and practices. As man makes increasing demands on living things to furnish him with food, fiber, and recreation, he must make wise decisions to stem the rate at which living things are used. Also, if he is to live in harmony with his fellow man, he must learn to respect all forms of life. His early experiences with plants and animals can help to develop such an attitude.

SOME IMPORTANT
OBJECTIVES

*ATTITUDES AND APPRECIATIONS
TO BE ENCOURAGED:*
Basic to man's respect for his fellow man is a respect for *all* living things, no matter how lowly or insignificant they seem.

No creature is, in itself, harmful or beneficial; it is so only in terms of how it affects man's well-being.

Many creatures that at first seem uninteresting or repulsive become fascinating and even beautiful as they become familiar.

We are animals whose bodies are marvelous machines that can be studied without special equipment and without physical harm.

Since nearly all plants and animals live in complex associations with one another and with their environment, the consequences of any major action on them must be carefully considered.

Decay after death is not unfortunate and ugly; it is essential to put back into circulation the substances needed for the living.

There are so many kinds of living things and they live in so many kinds of places that anyone who is interested can find out something new and exciting about them.

*SKILLS AND HABITS
TO BE DEVELOPED:*
Noticing plants and animals that might escape the eye of a less informed observer

Relating the age and growth of a felled tree to the appearance of its stump, and pieces of wood to their position in the logs from which they were cut

Setting up and maintaining a small aquarium containing a few wild plants and animals borrowed from a pond

Using a hand magnifier (and a microscope, when available) to observe small living things

Recognizing the factors that affect decay and modifying these to speed or slow decay, depending upon circumstances

Setting up a controlled experiment with living things and using many individuals for increasing the validity of the results

Making a random sample of a population and using it to count or to describe the whole

Working with others in carrying out an investigation and in gathering and analyzing data cooperatively

Using correctly terms such as insect (versus bug), fruit (versus seed), larva, sample, opposing, annual layer, decay, scavenger, predator, overproduction, radial, mold, and spore

*FACTS AND PRINCIPLES
TO BE TAUGHT:*
Humans are animals whose skeletons, muscles, eyes, and other body parts are in many ways similar to those of dogs or cats.

Most muscles of backboned animals work in opposing pairs, one muscle moving a body part in one direction, the other returning it.

All aquatic animals need oxygen. Some get it by coming to the surface; others have gills and get it directly from the water.

By producing far more offspring than can grow to maturity, living things perpetuate themselves in spite of unfavorable conditions or calamities; those that do not may become extinct.

All plants and animals produce young, and do so in a variety of ways—mostly by seeds, spores, or eggs, but also by growing directly connected to the body of an adult.

Woody plants grow in length only near their tips, but they grow in diameter throughout their stems and roots.

Besides needing moisture and warmth, molds need food on which to grow, because they cannot make their own food as green plants do.

Decay is speeded not only by bacteria and molds but also by many small animals whose activity often goes unnoticed.

Spiders are amazingly numerous, have predictable habits, and indirectly may be of great help to man.

THE BETTER
TO SEE WITH

Some animals have two eyes facing forward like ours; others, such as rabbits, robins, chickens, or goldfish, have their eyes at the side. *Which are better to see with?*

Let the pupils choose partners and play catch with ping-pong, styrofoam, or other light balls. The teams should record each time they catch the ball cleanly and each time they fumble or drop it. At a signal, all the pupils should close one eye and continue playing catch, still keeping a record of catches and of fumbles or drops. *How does the record of catches using both eyes compare with the record of catches using only one eye? Can you see why there are almost no one-eyed players in major league baseball?*

Have each pupil close one eye and look at some object in the room. Then have him open that eye and close the other, alternating in rapid succession. *Does the scene look the same when viewed with each eye? Which objects seem to shift the most?*

Have the pupils keep the left eye closed and look at the same scene as before, while blinking the right eye. *Does the scene shift as before?* A person sees a slightly different view with each eye. This difference helps us to tell how far away various objects are.

While each pupil keeps looking straight ahead, have him stretch his arms out to the side and wiggle his fingers. *Without turning eyes or head, how far back can the hands be moved before they disappear from sight?*

Now have the pupils look at rabbits, robins, chickens, and goldfish, or at pictures of these animals. *Where are their eyes located in*

comparison with ours? Would a rabbit see most things with one eye or two? Does this help it tell distance? How far back do you think a rabbit could see without turning its head? Would it be easier to sneak up on a rabbit or a person? If you had a choice, would you rather see like a rabbit or like a person?

MUSCLE TEAMS

Nearly all muscles work in pairs. One of the pair pulls a part of the body in one direction; the other pulls it in the opposite direction. Muscles act by becoming shorter, but they cannot expand by themselves. When one contracts and then relaxes, it needs a partner to pull it back. Pupils can learn how muscles work in teams by examining some muscles in their own bodies as follows:

While seated at your desk, place your right hand under the desk and lift up. At the same time, use your left hand to feel the muscles of your right arm, above your elbow. Where the muscles are hard, they have contracted. Where they are soft, they are relaxed and long. *Which muscles are acting to lift your forearm?*

Now move your right hand to the top of the desk and press down. Feel the muscles as before. *Which ones are contracted? Which are relaxed? Do they feel the same as they did when you were lifting?*

Next, rest your foot flat on the floor in front of you, pressing it down hard enough so it won't slide easily. Put one hand on the muscles at the front (top) of your thigh and the other on the muscles at the back of your thigh. Try to slide your foot away from you. *Which muscles contract? Which are relaxed?*

Try pulling your foot toward you. *Can you feel the change in the muscles?* Push and pull your foot back and forth several times and note how the muscles alternately contract and relax.

Try other movements of your body and see if you can find the opposing sets of muscles. *Can you feel the muscles that close your jaws? Where are the ones that open them?*

Some muscle teams are not so easy to find. *Where are the ones that enable you to stick out your tongue? How can a worm make itself long and slender?* (Hint: Try rolling a ball of clay into a long, thin "worm.") *Where do you think the muscles are that cause it to get this shape?*

THE LAWS OF JAWS

Food

When pupils use their hands to imitate the action of their jaws or those of a dog, they are apt to make both hands move up and down. But if they investigate how their own jaws and those of other backboned animals really work, they may be surprised to learn that their hands do not show how jaws work at all.

Pass a cracker to each pupil. Let him break it in two and put half in his mouth to chew while he rests his forehead against the edge of his desk. *Is it easy or difficult to chew like this? Is it natural for the jaws to move this way?*

After he swallows the first half, ask him to chew the second half, but this time while he rests his chin on the desk. *Is it easy or difficult to chew now? When the lower jaw cannot move, what must the head do to chew?*

Ask the pupils to observe other vertebrate animals (ones with back- bones) such as dogs, cats, horses, cows, fish, turtles, and birds. *In all these animals, which jaw moves in chewing—the upper, the lower, or both?* Ask any pupil who can do so to observe an alligator feeding at the zoo. *Do its jaws work the same way as our own?*

A snake's jaws are different from ours, making it possible for the snake to swallow prey larger than its own head. There are elastic connections between its upper and lower jaws which let the jaws separate. Also, the right and left halves of the lower jaw can be spread apart to help in swallowing. Arrange to have your class watch a snake as it swallows something big. *In how many ways do its jaws operate differently from ours? Similarly to ours?*

Now ask each pupil to bring in a grasshopper or a beetle, both of which are chewing insects, and look carefully through a magnifier at the insect's jaws. *In what ways are they similar to our own? In what ways are they different?*

LOG
LAYERS

Good teaching is not simply giving information. Pupils should learn a great deal by observing things for themselves. They can learn much from a cut-down tree or a stump, for example. For just this purpose

some stumps should be left on the school grounds.

Let pupils examine the cut surface to see the rings. *How many are there?* To keep track, they may stick a pin bearing a small paper "flag" into every tenth one. A magnifying glass will help.

If one ring was formed each year, how old was the tree? Let a pupil outline in crayon its size when he was born. *Was it living in 1900? In Lincoln's time? Can you find a still older stump?*

The rings that one sees in a stump or log are really the edges of *layers* of wood. These layers nest inside each other, somewhat like upside-down ice-cream cones in a stack. However, they taper much more gradually than these cones, and are far more irregular, with extensions going out into the branches and twigs.

If possible, have pupils count the layers in several pieces of a cut-up tree trunk and branches. *Why does their number vary so?*

Also let pupils examine scraps of wood that show log layers clearly and then find the layers in solid wood furniture. *How many years of growth does each piece represent? What positions did the various pieces have in the logs before they were sawed? What may have caused some layers to be thicker than others?*

What do log layers look like in plywood? If pupils read about how veneer and plywood are made, they can understand why these layers often produce interesting patterns in these materials.

How could someone prove that each layer in a tree represents one year's growth? How might one discover why the layers differ in thickness? (Sections of wood can be cut from living trees without harming them with a tool called an *increment borer.*)

AGED IN WOOD

In "Log Layers" you read how trees form successive layers of wood that show as rings in stumps and in the ends of logs. After pupils have studied a stump, a fence post, or a log, they should examine other objects made of wood to see the annual rings or layers in them. Some of these objects can be found in your classroom, some in other rooms at school, and some at home.

Ask a few of the class to bring in baseball bats. Let all the pupils examine the handle ends of the bats. *How many years of wood does each handle represent?* Trace the layers of wood through the handle and into the head of each bat. *Can you see where parts of some layers have been cut off in shaping the bat?*

In solid wood tables such as some library tables and work benches, the tops are often made from several boards fastened together. Look at the ends of some of these boards to see which has

the "oldest" wood. Look for other boards whose ends show annual layers. Some cupboards, the card catalogue in the library, some desk tops, and even freshly sharpened wooden pencils show annual layers. *What is the "oldest" board you can find in the room? What is the "oldest" board you can find in the school? Can you find a board whose wood took just as long to grow as you did?*

When the pupils have studied annual layers in the ends of boards, let them examine the lines, wiggly or straight, on the flat surface of boards. See if they can trace this grain to the layers in the ends of the boards. (*Note:* Wooden veneer may be too thin to show distinct annual layers at its ends. Use thicker wood.)

Get a few scrap pieces of two-by-four or two-by-six from a carpenter at a construction site or from a lumber yard. Give each pupil one to examine. *How long did it take to grow the wood from which each scrap was cut? How far from the center of the tree did the wood in each scrap grow?*

LIMB
LIFT

When a pupil grows, he grows all over. *Do woody plants grow in the same manner?* Some interesting observations and activities will help to give the answer and will change opinions, too.

First, ask the class if tree limbs,

like pupils' arms, get lifted higher as a tree grows. Record their opinions. Then set up the following committees to study the question: Swing, Fence, Vine, Trunk, and Seedling. Ask the Swing Committee to investigate, both by interview and by direct observation, whether swings hanging from limbs must be lengthened from time to time as the trees grow.

Ask the Fence Committee to look for fence wires that have been nailed to tree trunks. *Are old fences (whose wires go through a tree instead of being outside the bark) higher than new ones? Do farmers have to lower old fences from time to time?*

The Vine Committee should examine vines growing on buildings or other structures to see if the vines move their stems as they grow, refastening them to higher places. Mark a vine and the wall behind it at the same level. *Do the marks move apart in the course of a week or a month during the growing season?*

The Trunk Committee should stick two pins, one a few feet above the other, in each of several tree trunks and then measure the distance between the pins each week during the growing season. *How much does the distance change during this time?*

The Seedling Committee should make ink marks an inch apart on the stem of a seedling (such as a lima bean plant several inches tall) and then measure the distance between marks as the plant grows. *Do the marks all move apart at the same rate? Where must new marks be made?*

Finally, let the committees report their findings. *What parts of woody plants grow fastest, according to the records? Do woody plants really grow as people do?*

SEED SURPLUS

An important principle of science is that most plants and animals produce far more offspring than are able to grow up. To make this idea more meaningful to pupils, let them discover how many seeds a single plant can produce. Many common weeds work well for this, especially in the fall, before their seeds are scattered.

First bring in a large weed with seeds, and ask the pupils to write down their estimates of the number. Then have them collect all its seeds and determine the number more accurately. They may count out groups of 10 or 100, or they may divide the seeds into piles of equal size, perhaps thimblefuls, count those in a few piles to get an average, and multiply this by the number of piles. Otherwise, with a sensitive balance they can find out how many seeds it takes to weigh as much as a small nail and then how many nail-weights of seeds there are in the entire lot.

It is not good science to generalize on the basis of *one* sample. Therefore, let each pupil find the number of seeds on a separate plant of the same kind, chosen at *random* —not just the biggest one he can find. A class can get a random sampling by spreading out across a weedy area and then picking the nearest specimen of a particular kind of weed when you call, "Stop!" All the individual estimates can then be used to find the *average* number of seeds produced by plants of that species in that particular place and year. A class can do this for several species, or committees may be responsible for different kinds of weeds.

What would happen if all these seeds grew into plants and the plants in turn produced seeds, all of which grew, and so on? Why would all the seeds not be likely to produce full-grown plants? Would some have a better chance of growing than others? If so, which ones? How many seeds actually do grow when planted? Pupils can find out by planting 100 in a pan of soil.

BURDOCK

TEASEL

QUEEN ANNE'S LACE

FISH-LESS AQUARIUMS

Pint jars make excellent aquariums for pond life if fish, turtles, and other large animals are left out. *Each* pupil should have one of his own to watch and enjoy—even if the window sills and book shelves are filled for a time! Then every pupil can make his own observations and compare what he finds with what his classmates find, instead of merely becoming used to a conventional classroom aquarium that too often is just part of the furniture.

Ideally, pupils should set up their aquariums at a nearby pond—bits of the pond borrowed for a short while. Early fall is a good time to do this. Then the experience may be repeated in the spring to see what seasonal changes have occurred.

In making a trip to the pond, it may be feasible for a primary teacher and an upper-grade teacher to take their classes at the same time, letting each older pupil be responsible for a younger one. It is surprising how well they shoulder this responsibility! One or two parents, too, may be invited along to learn about the activities of the children, as well as to provide additional supervision. Notes should be sent home in advance to advise about clothing, particularly boots or rubbers.

If the class cannot be taken to the pond, you or some pupils helped by parents can bring the materials to school. For a class of 30 pupils obtain about 4 gallons of pond water, a small pail of sand or silt from the pond bottom, and a gallon jar containing pond plants and animals. Gather a *few* handfuls of small plants from near the shore. Then add snails, water insects, and other small animals collected by drawing a large kitchen strainer along the bottom. If each sample is first dumped into a white enameled pan, the animals can more easily be seen against the white background. Then they can be spooned out and placed in the jar. Later, at school, the plants and animals may be transferred to shallow enameled pans so that pupils can select the ones they want.

To set up his aquarium, each pupil should put about an inch of pond-bottom sediment in his jar, stick in a sprig or two of water plant, and fill the jar with pond water. Then he may add a snail or two and a *few* water insects. The water will clear if it is not disturbed, and he will probably see many tiny animals that he did not notice previously. A magnifying glass will be helpful.

So that the experience will be pleasant, be sure that pupils:

1. Put in only a *few* plants and animals, and lean toward having *too* few. Crowding only causes them to die and stink.

2. Keep the aquariums in a cool

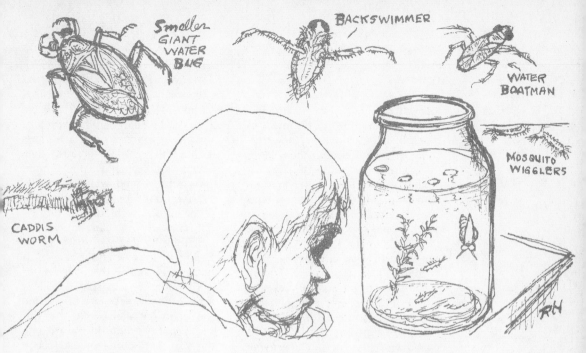

place, away from radiators and, for the most part, out of direct sunlight.

3. Disturb the jars as little as possible.

4. Do not add food. The animals eat plants or other animals, and the green plants make their own food.

5. Add pond water as needed, not chlorinated tap water.

Pupils will be fascinated by what they discover—water fleas darting about; young snails hatching from eggs; diving beetles carrying their own air supply; plants giving off tiny streams of bubbles; hydra capturing small creatures by means of tentacles; caddis worms pulling their "houses" along; and mosquito wigglers hanging from the surface and later turning into winged adults.

Let the class investigate and discuss such questions as these:

1. *How do the various animals move? Which have legs, which crawl without apparent legs, and which remain attached to objects?*

2. *What do the animals eat, and how do they eat? By what means do they avoid being eaten by other animals?*

3. *How do the animals seem to get air? Which carry bubbles with them or stick breathing tubes above the water? Which have moving gills? Do any have no apparent means of getting air?*

4. *If you darken the jar with a paper bag for a half hour and then uncover it, what can you see that you did not notice before?*

5. *What signs of growth do the plants show? Which parts grow most—leaves, stems, or roots? Do all the plants have these parts?*

After a week or so, before interest wanes, take another trip to the pond for the express purpose of returning the creatures to the environment from which they were borrowed, instead of washing them down the drain or throwing them out. This helps to instill a respect for living things, a basic attitude of conservation.

STICKY TRAPS

Many living things can be brought into the classroom, but some can be studied better where they normally live. Spiders and their webs, for example, are observed best in gardens, in shrubbery, or in dark corners of buildings where things are undisturbed. To help your pupils appreciate what an amazing structure a spider's web is, encourage them to investigate some webs as follows:

Look for an orb (round) web that is nearly perfect, indicating that it was recently made. *Is the web more nearly horizontal or vertical? Which would be better for catching flying insects? On what part of the web does the spider rest?* If it isn't on the web, see if you can find its hiding place. *Can you find how it can tell when something is caught in the web?*

Lightly touch each of the different kinds of silk making up the web —the main supporting lines, the radial (spokelike) lines, and the apparently circular ones. *Which are sticky enough to hold a fly?* Follow one of the apparently circular lines. *Does it join itself to make a circle, or does it form part of a spiral?* If you can catch a fly, toss it into the sticky threads, then watch to see how the spider approaches it and wraps it in silk.

Now look for a funnel web. Often these are hidden in bushes, tall grass, or in dark corners of buildings, so that you may need a flashlight to examine one. *Is a funnel web sticky like an orb web?*

The funnel-web spider usually waits in the throat of its funnel and then darts out after prey that alights on its web. Probe downward into the rear of the funnel and see if you can make its occupant come out. *Does it walk or run out? Does it have the same number of legs as other kinds of spiders you have observed?*

Finally, look for a spider lowering itself on a single thread. *Is the thread sticky? If the spider is made to scramble back up, what does it do with the thread?*

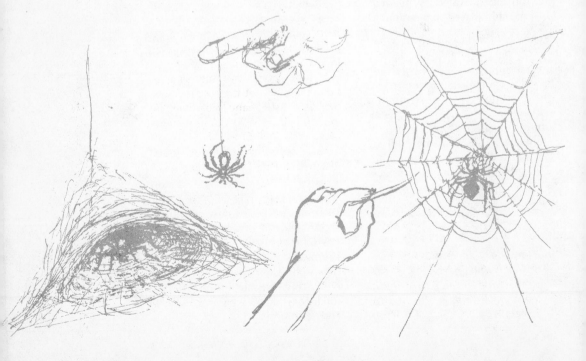

LIVING FUZZ

To most pupils the word *plant* may suggest "green," "seeds," or "flowers." But there are many plants that are not green, do not come from seeds, and do not have flowers. Yet they are interesting to study and some are easy to grow. Molds are one such group.

Ask the pupils to bring in some samples of home-baked goods such as bread, cake, or rolls (store bread usually has a chemical to inhibit molds) and some fruits such as berries, grapes, or plums. In class, give each pupil two plastic sandwich bags. Have him write his name on two slips of paper and put one in each bag.

Next, have each pupil moisten *slightly* a piece of bread or cake and put it in one bag. In the other have him put a sample of fruit. Then have all twist their bags shut and fasten them with rubber bands. Provide a carton for each row and let the pupils put their bags in it. Then set the cartons in a warm, dark place.

In three days, or after a week-end, let the pupils remove the bags and examine their contents without opening them. *Has any fuzz appeared? Does it appear just on the food, or on the plastic, too? Which of all the samples has the most fuzz? What color is it?*

If fuzz is not yet apparent, put the bags back for a few more days and then take them out once more. *Is the fuzz bigger now? Do you know of any nonliving things that increase like this in a few days without anything having been added to them?*

Without removing the samples from the bags, let the class examine the fuzz with hand magnifiers or microscopes. *What does it look like when magnified? What changes have occurred in the food itself?* Put the bags away for another week and see what happens.

The fuzz is a mold that grows from microscopic *spores* that drift in the air. Some land on foods, and if conditions are right, they grow into fuzzy or powdery plants. Most are harmless, but it is probably best to discard the bags, unopened, when you are finished with them.

BURYING BEETLE

MAGGOT

SANITATION SQUAD

When plants or animals die, the materials in them must be made available to living plants and animals for use. Otherwise, there would result a shortage of the substances needed for life. Decay is one process by which once-living plants and animals become food for living ones, either by being eaten directly or by being returned to the soil, water, and air. Pupils should have an opportunity to observe what happens to an animal after it dies and to see some of the creatures that help speed this important process of decay.

To provide this opportunity, get a freshly killed mouse, bird, or other small animal (as may sometimes be found along the highway), or a 1/2-pound piece of raw meat. Go out with your class and place it on the ground at some distance from the school building, where it will not likely be disturbed by people. Cover it with a piece of 1/2-inch mesh hardware cloth, staking down the corners firmly so that dogs and cats will not dig up and carry off the carcass.

Take your class to visit the carcass each day for two weeks and then weekly for a month or two. Let the pupils observe and record as best they can its changes and the visitors to it.

When does the carcass first become smelly? How soon do flies visit it? How do you suppose they found it? (Let some of the class test their suggestions by experimenting!) *What parts show the first signs of decay? What parts do you think will be the last ones to decay?*

At each visit, let the pupils loosen the stakes and use a stick to turn over the carcass. *What kinds of creatures are at work beneath it? Do they seem upset at being uncovered? Where might they have come from, and how could they have located the food?*

These animals are part of an efficient sanitation squad, most of whom work unseen—inside or under a carcass, or at night when they themselves are less likely to become food for bigger animals.

everyday things

Such things as paper clips, shoeboxes, marbles, candles, bread, clay, string, and scraps of wood constitute a veritable reservoir of materials for teaching science. They cost little or nothing, yet are often better than expensive items for providing worthwhile experiences. They encourage youngsters to get involved and to use their ingenuity, rather than merely to operate ready-made equipment. Already familiar to pupils, commonplace things like these seldom block or distract their thinking in the way strange and complicated apparatus often does.

Many useful odds and ends are available in quantity, enabling all children to engage in explorations, rather than limiting them to watching demonstrations. They permit experiments to be repeated and modified easily. Usually obtainable on short notice, they do not necessitate requisitions, administrative approval, and the delays which too often postpone the arrival of commercial equipment beyond the interest span of children.

With everyday things, pupils need not stop learning science at the close of school, since many of these items are also available around the home. There the children can repeat the experiences they had in school—and then continue with their own ideas and with suggestions from books. Even parents can become involved and not only refresh their understanding of science but also become better acquainted with what the school is doing.

Everyday things can help to provide for individual differences among children—differences in interest, attitude, creativity, dexterity, and academic aptitude. They can be as intriguing and challenging to slow learners and poor readers as to gifted pupils. They enable youngsters to learn with their hands as well as with their minds; yet they place no ceiling on ingenuity or industry.

forces and motions

7

Children are constantly having experiences with things that move—balls, hammers, automobiles, creeks, and wind, to name but a few—and during their lifetimes they will continue to use, enjoy, and avoid moving objects. Consequently, they should have a basic understanding of motions and changes in motion, and of the forces responsible for these changes.

Since many forces and motions are easy to control and measure, the principles that apply to them are among the best understood in science. Tested countless times, they seem to apply universally—not only everywhere on earth but in space, too, as shown by accurate predictions of the motions of planets and satellites. These principles are invaluable for explaining many kinds of actions, from those in a game of marbles to the orbiting of space capsules.

Yet, in spite of what is known, many false notions persist, and these handicap people in their comprehension of the environment. One such notion is that even if there were no friction or gravity, objects would have to be pushed or pulled continually to keep them going. Another is that a person in a vehicle is "thrown" backward when it starts, forward when it stops, and to one side as it turns—whereas, like *all* objects, he merely tends to maintain, without change, whatever motion he has. Still another is that a pony pulls a cart or a lady pushes a carriage—when, in each case, *both* objects pull or push on each other, *equally* hard!

With today's emphasis on speed and with the tragic toll that results when natural laws are disregarded, it is imperative that pupils acquire a sound understanding of the principles of motion and the realization that, unlike man-made laws, they cannot be ignored without predictable and often disastrous results. With this kind of training, everyone will have a safer and more pleasant life.

SOME IMPORTANT
OBJECTIVES

*ATTITUDES AND APPRECIATIONS
TO BE ENCOURAGED:*

Man progresses in his understanding of the environment by recognizing basic factors in situations, such as force, motion, and mass, and by extracting general principles which apply to *all* situations in which these factors are involved.

The same principles involving forces and motions seem to apply in all places on earth, as well as everywhere in space.

By mastering relatively few basic principles of forces and motions, one can explain many events that are often seemingly unrelated.

Physical laws, unlike man-made laws, are unvarying; thus, if a speeding automobile hits something, the result is the same whether a policeman is present or not.

Some fundamental concepts relating to forces and motions still are not well understood; examples include the nature of mass and of gravitational, magnetic, and electric forces, and the reason objects tend to maintain whatever direction and speed they have.

Many factors in our environment, such as friction, speed, and mass, have both advantageous and disadvantageous consequences.

High speed is dangerous because it makes possible sudden changes in motion, and these often cause damage, injury, and death.

*SKILLS AND HABITS
TO BE DEVELOPED:*

Identifying pairs of pushes and of pulls in the environment and the effects they have on the objects on which they act

Noting and describing changes in the speed and direction of motion of objects and relating these to the forces on the objects

Estimating the relative masses of objects from the ease with which the objects are made to move by pushes or pulls

Comparing the amount of friction between objects as they rub together and as they roll

Measuring the friction between various pairs of materials

Using screw drivers, wrenches, pliers, shears, and other tools properly to increase the effectiveness of manual forces

Carrying out tests which are valid and keeping alert for any factors which may cause test results to be of doubtful validity

Showing differences in quantities, and relationships between pairs of quantities, by simple graphs

Suggesting hypotheses to account for events, and testing them

Making full use of one's imagination, ingenuity, and creativity

Using properly such terms as force, mass, friction, pulley, turning effect, pivot, force arm, reaction, and center of weight

*FACTS AND PRINCIPLES
TO BE TAUGHT:*

A push or pull is necessary to start an object moving and to change the direction or speed, or both, of one that is moving.

Moving objects keep going straight unless acted on by sidewise pushes or pulls which make them change direction.

A force exerted by one object on a second is always accompanied by an equal and opposite force exerted by the second object on the first.

How easily an object can be

made to move depends on the amount of stuff in it, its *mass;* its weight also depends on its mass.

Whenever two objects touch, there is friction between them, and this tends to hinder any motion of one along the other.

Friction between two objects in contact is less when one rolls along the other than when they rub.

Objects held together by friction, or fastened firmly, act as one object, of combined mass, when pushed or pulled along.

Ropes and pulleys are means of multiplying forces on objects and therefore are often used to move heavy things.

The turning effect of a force depends, in part, on how far the force is from the pivot or axle of the object to which it is applied.

BALANCED BOXES

It is fascinating to observe the reactions of young pupils when they are confronted by something contrary to common experience. One such thing is a curiously balanced box that has been set up in the classroom before they arrive.

Firmly stick a lump of modeling clay inside one corner of a quart milk carton or a cereal box. Then set the box on a high shelf or cabinet, with the unweighted part extending far out over the edge; or prop it up with a block so it leans way over without tipping. Do this after school, when all pupils have left.

The next day watch what happens when the children notice the box. *Why doesn't it topple?* Get them to offer explanations before looking inside it. These explanations constitute simple *hypotheses* which they invent to account for the curious behavior of the box. It may be worth making a tape recording of their comments to play back later, after they have looked inside the box.

Another approach is to let them rig other cartons to act like the one on display—*without help and without first looking inside it.* For this, have many light boxes on hand and a variety of such things as blocks, rubber bands, scrap hardware, string, stones, modeling clay, magnets, tape, glue or cement, and nails.

The box is able to stay in this position because it and the clay are essentially one object, with most of its weight far off center. It is helpful to imagine the weight to be concentrated at a single point near the clay, or even inside it. This point may be called the *center of weight.* (The usual term is *center of gravity,* but a child's concept of *weight* is more simple and direct than that of *gravity.*)

As long as its center of weight is supported and cannot fall, the carton-and-clay combination stays put. *What happens, however, when its center of weight is able to move to a lower position?*

RUBS
AND ROLLS

Whenever one object rubs or slides against another, the friction between them tends to retard the motion, and is often a hindrance. Pupils can easily discover one of the best ways to reduce such friction—by substituting rolling for sliding.

Have them put some blocks in a shoebox on a table, and pull it along by a slender rubber band fastened to one end. Then let them set the box on 10 or more parallel drinking straws to serve as rollers, and pull the rubber band. *What makes the difference?*

For a valid test, the situations being compared must be alike *in every respect but one. Is this true if the box slides on* varnish, *but rolls on* paper? *How can the test be made more fair?* Let pupils suggest ways and then try them. One way is to pull the box, first *across* the straws so that they roll, and then *parallel* to them so that they and the box slide. Another is to paste down one set of straws, or flatten them, so that they cannot roll.

Pupils can make similar tests with round toothpicks and flat ones, with whole marbles and marbles that have cracked in half, and with uncooked macaroni of various shapes. They may also:

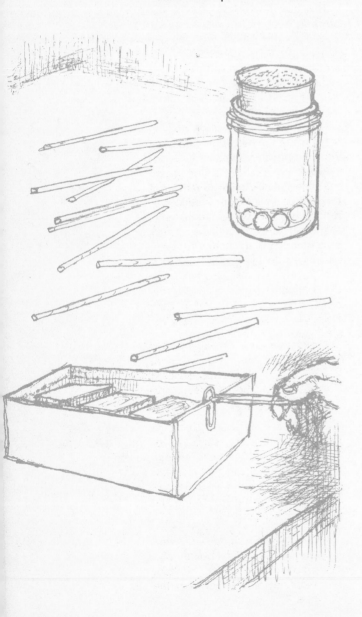

1. Roll a skate down a playground slide, and then fasten its wheels with tape so that they cannot turn and place it on the slide.

2. Fill a tall, slender can with sand, set it in a slightly wider glass jar, and spin it; then put a circle of glass marbles in the jar, set the can on them, and spin it again.

3. Pull a friend on a sled along a concrete walk and then pull him in a wagon having steel wheels without rubber tires.

4. Watch boxes being unloaded from a truck onto an incline having many rollers, and then try a box on a playground slide.

5. Ask at a garage for old ball and roller bearings that have been cleaned and see how they substitute rolling for rubbing.

FRICTION
CUBES

Whenever objects press against each other, there is friction between them. This varies in amount, depending in part on the materials in contact. To discover this for themselves, pupils can experiment with friction cubes, in teams of five or six.

At a lumber yard have a four-by-four sawed accurately into cubes, one for each team. Then ask each pupil to bring in one or more scrap pieces of linoleum, floor tile, carpet, inner-tube rubber, foam plastic, sandpaper, cloth, aluminum foil, leather, or other flat material. Help each team to cut squares of different materials to fit on the faces of their cube, and to cement or glue them on smoothly. Have them trim the edges so that the cube rests on only one material at a time. They may leave one face of the cube uncovered, to provide a surface of bare wood.

Now each team member, in turn, sets the cube on a smooth board with his material down. He gradually raises one end of the board until the cube just starts to slide. Then he measures and records the height of the raised end, and checks this a few times. This height gives an indication of the friction between the board and his material. If the board is placed on a chalk tray, the height of its raised end can easily be marked on the chalkboard.

A team may show by a bar graph the average height to which the board must be raised for each material to slide. They may also:

1. Test the cube on various surfaces, including painted wood, plastic- or rubber-covered wood, cardboard, metal, and glass.

2. Compare the friction between two unwaxed surfaces of wood with that between two waxed ones, using a block and a board, each waxed on one side only, and weighting the block with a brick.

3. Slide down a playground slide on pieces of cardboard, plywood, foil, plastic, cotton, wool, nylon, leather, and the like.

PAPER-CLIP CRANKS

Handlebars, pencil sharpeners, and doorknobs are just a few of the many everyday things designed to enable small forces to have great turning effects. With paper clips, pupils, working in pairs, can readily discover the principle involved in these things.

First give each pair a paper clip to straighten out. Then have one pupil hold one end, and his partner the other, and each try to make the wire turn in the other's fingers without bending it. *If both squeeze the wire hard, can either one turn it easily?*

Now ask one pupil to bend the wire at a right angle, about an inch from his end. Then have him turn the bent part as a crank, while his partner squeezes his end of the wire and tries to turn it in the opposite direction. *Who is more successful?*

Next have the partner with the longer part of the wire use *it* as a crank. Also suggest that the pair make and try cranks of still other lengths. *Which enables a force to have the greater turning effect, a long crank or a short one? Does it matter at what distance from the axle one applies his force to a crank?*

Finally, pupils may make a second bend in some of the cranks, to form handles. These make the cranks more convenient to turn.

These simple activities show that the turning effect of a force depends not only on the strength of the force but also on how far from the axle or pivot the force is applied. This distance is called the *force arm*. A crank is simply a means of providing a longer force arm, so that a force has a greater turning effect.

What other common devices depend on this principle? Have the class make a list and add to it each day. Also let them post pictures of tools and other devices that are turned, indicating the pivot or axle of each by a red dot or line and the turning by a circular arrow showing where and how the force is applied.

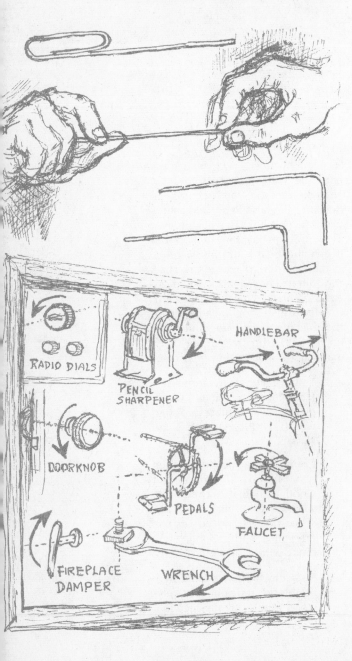

RADIO DIALS

PENCIL SHARPENER

HANDLEBAR

DOORKNOB

PEDALS

FAUCET

FIREPLACE DAMPER

WRENCH

BROOMSTICK PULLEYS

Pulleys often change the direction of pulls, as when a flag is raised by pulling the rope down, and they may also multiply pulls. Pulleys made from a broomstick will help to show why this is so and will surprise pupils by making them amazingly "strong."

Saw a discarded broomstick in half, and give the pieces to two pupils whose masses (and, therefore, weights) are obviously different. Set two chairs a few feet apart, with their backs toward each other, and let the pupils sit on them, facing each other and holding their sticks by both ends, at arm's length.

Caution: Have them wear gloves to avoid chafing their hands.

Tie one end of a clothesline to the center of the stick held by the pupil of smaller mass, loop it around the center of the other stick, and bring it over the shoulder of the smaller pupil. Then ask a third pupil to pull on the rope while the others hold their sticks tightly and lift their feet. *Whose chair slides? Does the same chair slide when the seated pupils have exchanged places? Why does this happen?* Be sure the class notes that the rope pulls *singly* on the first stick, but *doubly* on the second. *If the rope is pulled 6 feet, how far does the chair move?*

Now pass the rope around the first stick so that *three* strands pull on it, and only *two* on the other. *Which chair do you think will move?* Let pupils check, taking turns sitting and pulling. *How far does the chair slide when the rope is pulled 6 feet?*

When someone pulls on a rope with a force of, say, 10 pounds, his

pull acts all along the rope. If the rope goes around a stick, both strands pull on the stick, and the total pull is 20 pounds—reduced somewhat by friction. (Real pulleys turn with the rope, and thus make friction less.) *What would be the total pull if the rope is tied to a stick and goes around it once as well?*

WHIRLED WATER

Many children have seen someone swing a pail of water around without having it spill. Some have also seen a spin drier, in which clothes are whirled around in a drum with holes in it. The same principle—often misunderstood—is involved in both cases.

In teaching this principle it is good to start by giving a few pupils paper cups, and strings about 6 feet long. Let each pupil tie the ends of a string to two nail holes in a cup, made opposite each other and near the top. Then, preferably outdoors, have them add water and swing the cups around in various ways. Let the others try this, too. *Does any water spill out of a cup as long as it is kept whirling?*

Then have a pupil poke a small nail hole in the bottom of each cup, add some water, and whirl the cup around. *Does water come out of the hole even when the cup is bottomside up in its orbit? Will the cup empty faster when swung around, or when held still?*

Next, let pupils poke many nail holes in the bottom and side of each cup, from the inside, put in a wet rag, and again whirl it around. *Why does the rag not go off with the water?*

Now have someone hold up each string so that the cup on it hangs free, twist it around many times, and then put a very wet rag in the cup and let go. *What happens when the cup gets spinning fast?*

It is often said that "centrifugal force" keeps water from spilling out of a container that is being whirled around. It is also said that water is "pulled out" of the clothes in a spin drier by "centrifugal force." Unfortunately, these statements are erroneous, based on misconceptions. However, pupils can be helped to understand the *correct* concept of what is involved by having them take part in the following series of activities:

1. Roll a marble across a smooth, level table. *What kind of path does it follow? All* moving objects tend to do this, including bowling balls, hockey pucks, and rain drops. They go straight, unless pushed or pulled sideways out of a straight line.

2. Blow on the marble from the side as it rolls along slowly. *How is its motion changed by the push of the air? Does the marble continue to change direction after you stop blowing on it?*

3. Ask someone to hold a strip of thin cardboard, on edge, on the table and curve it gently. Then roll a marble along the inside of the curve. *Why does it not follow a straight path? What will happen if the curved cardboard is quickly lifted straight up as the marble rolls along it?* Try this, and see!

4. Roll a marble around in a round cardboard box cover. *What would the marble do if there were no rim to push against it?*

5. Poke a hole in the center of the cover and set it on a 78 rpm. record player turntable so that it lies flat. Put a few marbles in it, and start the motor. *What would the marbles do if the rim did not push inward against them? How could one check?*

6. Cut a few gaps in the rim of the cover, just big enough for the marbles to fit through. Then start the cover turning on the record player, and put some marbles in it. *What does a marble do if it happens to be at one of the gaps?* The rim of the cover acts like the drum of a spin drier, while the gaps represent holes in the drum, and the marbles behave like drops of water.

7. Wrap a narrow strip of cloth, about 7 inches long, around the rim of a skate wheel, and hold it in place with a rubber band. Then wet the cloth and lay the skate on its side on a sheet of colored construction paper, with this wheel down. Now spin the wheel rapidly. *What kind of path does a water drop take after it leaves the spinning cloth? Does anything pull the drop away from the cloth, or does it simply keep going straight when it and the spinning cloth no longer adhere strongly enough?*

These experiences suggest that when a container of water is whirled around, *no* force keeps the water from falling out the top. The water simply *tends* to keep moving in the direction it is going at any instant, while the container keeps pulling it out of this straight path and makes it go in a new direction. However, where there is a hole in the bottom or side of the container the water *can* continue to go in a straight line. Similarly, in a spin drier, *the water is not pulled out of the clothes.* Instead, the drum pushes inward on the clothes, keeping them from going straight, with the water, and so *the clothes are pushed away from the water!*

PULLS
IN PAIRS

A basic principle of science, often misunderstood, is that a pull on something is always accompanied by an equal pull on something else, in the opposite direction. The same is true of pushes; they always occur in pairs, equal and opposite. Some simple experiences can help the pupils to comprehend this principle better.

Cut a long, thin rubber band and tape one end securely to a short edge of a shoebox. Tie the other end to a staple from a paper stapler. Do the same with a second, identical shoebox.

Place the boxes end to end on a smooth table, and hook one of the staples on the end of the other box. Then pull the boxes apart so the rubber stretches a few inches, and let them go *at exactly the same instant.* Let pupils try this, too, and measure the distances the boxes move. *How do they compare? What does this suggest about how hard the rubber band pulls on each box?*

Next, ask a custodian to cut two 10-inch strips of steel band from around a packing case. Slip a loop of thread over the ends of one strip to hold it in the shape of a U. Then tape one arm of this U, with the bend up, securely to the end of one shoebox. Tape the unbent strip to another identical shoebox, to make the two boxes as alike as possible.

Place the boxes end to end, with the bent strip between them, and snip the thread. *Are the boxes affected equally?* Let pupils try this many times, and test the other strip also. *Does either strip seem to push any harder on one box than on the other?*

The shoeboxes may be thought of as pupils, with rubber bands and steel strips for arms. *Accordingly, when you pull on another pupil, does your arm pull on him only, or does it pull equally hard on both of you? How about when you push on someone?* Matched pupils can check this while seated on swings, on sheets of cardboard on a waxed floor, and on wagons, sleds, or skateboards.

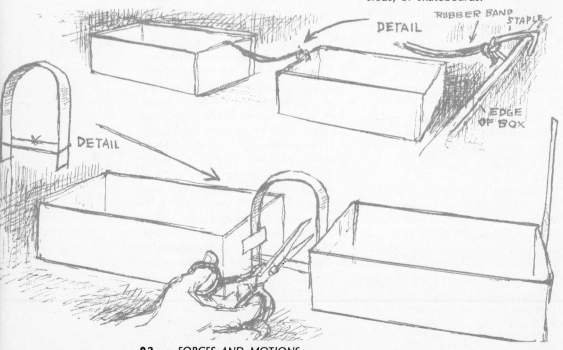

DETAIL

RUBBER BAND

STAPLE

DETAIL

EDGE OF BOX

DETAIL

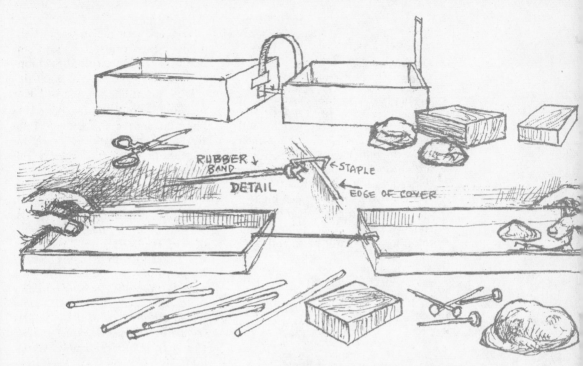

RUBBER BAND

DETAIL

←STAPLE

EDGE OF COVER

MASSES
AND MOTIONS

As a sequel to "Pulls in Pairs," pupils can easily investigate how the amount of stuff in objects affects how readily they can be made to move.

Use two identical shoeboxes or covers and have a cut rubber band pull them together. Then stick a wad of modeling clay firmly to the bottom of one. *Which is now moved more readily?* Let all pupils try this and note the effect of adding more and more clay on the motion of the box. The box and clay act as a single object which has more stuff, or *mass,* than the box alone.

Does the mass of a box also affect how readily it is moved when pushed, by a bent steel strip? Do nails or stones taped to a box also increase its mass and change how easily it is moved? Let pupils find out! To reduce the effect of friction, they may set the boxes on drinking-straw rollers. (See "Rubs and Rolls.")

When the boxes are empty, the rubber band pulls equally hard on both of them. Likewise, the steel strip pushes equally hard on both. *Is there any reason to think that the pulls or pushes on the two boxes are no longer equal when the masses of the boxes are different?* If not, then the difference in the motions of the boxes would seem to be related to their masses.

If two persons of considerably different mass sit on swings, skateboards, or wagons and gently pull or push on each other with a rope or stick, who will move more? Let pupils try this and see!

Later, let a pupil add clay to two shoeboxes until they are affected *equally* when pulled together by a rubber band. *Now how do their masses compare?* Then ask him to set *one* of the boxes on straws to serve as rollers, and let the rubber band pull on them. *What happens?* This occurs because friction holds one box and the table together and they then act as one object with combined mass. In fact, they form one mass with the entire earth!

REACTION CARTS

As a follow-up to "Masses and Motions," pupils can watch, and then make and test, carts which show the principle of rockets. These are propelled forward as other things are shot backward.

Cut two slits, 5 centimeters apart, in a short edge of an inverted shoebox cover. Slip a rubber band into them, stretch it back, and hold

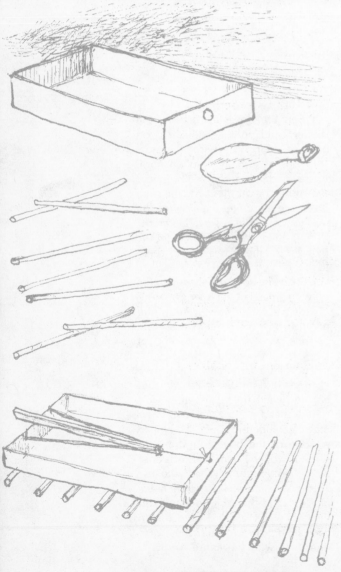

it with a thread fastened to the opposite end of the cover. Then rest a slender stick between the cuts, with one end against the stretched rubber band.

Now lay out many drinking straws on a table, parallel to each other, so that they act as rollers. Set the cover on them, ask everyone to stand back, and then snip the thread with scissors. *What happens? Why? On what two objects does the stretched rubber band act when released? How would the motions of these objects compare if they had equal masses and were retarded equally by friction?*

Next, make a 1-centimeter hole in one end of a light paper box. Blow up a fairly large balloon, hold it closed, and put its neck through the hole, mouth outward, so the lip is held firmly. Then set the box on a row of straws, and release the balloon. *What happens? On what two things does the stretched rubber act when the balloon is released? What happens to them as a result?*

The propulsion of the carts may be said to be due to *reaction*. The action of the stick, or air, and the accompanying reaction of the cart both result from a *pair* of forces exerted by the rubber.

Other illustrations of this principle include the retreat of a rowboat when someone steps from it to a dock, the rotation of a lawn sprinkler as a result of water pressure which causes streams of water to move in one direction and the sprinkler in the other, and the propulsion of a rocket when gases produced by the burning fuel push the rocket forward as they shoot backward.

**pupil
participation**

Inasmuch as firsthand experiences are fundamental to learning science, it follows that each pupil needs to have a rich variety of such experiences. Everyone, therefore, should participate in science activities, and no one need be a mere onlooker.

For example, every pupil can make a "Triple-can Balance" to use whenever he needs it. When studying magnetism, all the children can work with their own "Bobby-pin Compasses" rather than just watch the teacher demonstrate. Everyone can have his own animals and plants for close scrutiny, as in "Fish-less Aquariums." The entire class can contribute to the rounding of "Brick Pebbles." All can take turns in experimenting with "Masses and Motions," using materials placed on the science table.

Demonstrations should be used sparingly—chiefly to show pupils what to do or how to do it, and to perform those few things which are too difficult, dangerous, or expensive for everyone to try.

Having every pupil participate may, at times, raise problems —problems of time, materials, space, storage, and behavior. But these have solutions that are often obvious if the basic purposes of the teaching are kept clearly in mind. For example:

1. Attempt to "cover" less, but teach it better by giving pupils ample time and opportunity for firsthand experiences.

2. Make much use of everyday things such as cans, pebbles, nails, and vinegar—all available in quantity at little cost.

3. Use the playground, lawn, gymnasium, and corridor for science activities, as well as window sills and chalk trays.

4. Let pupils help store supplies in boxes, cans, and jars, and teach them to get the items as needed—and to put them back.

5. Keep pupils busy with worthwhile activities, and there will be little mischief—even though, perhaps, a bit more noise.

vibrations
and
sounds

8

Drums, whistles, and horns all attest to the fact that sounds are intrinsically appealing to children. Playing with sounds in school is great fun for them; yet they can learn while doing so. They can also learn by investigating the motions of objects that swing, bounce, and sway—motions which are like the vibrations that produce sounds, only slower.

Pupils should become aware that many familiar objects vibrate, at various rates and with different degrees of vigor. Through firsthand experiences they should learn that these vibrations depend upon factors which usually can be controlled and that sounds result when things vibrate at a high enough rate. They should understand the principles employed by musical instruments, so often used to make the air vibrate.

Children are aware of a great variety of sounds, clearly shown by the richness of their vocabulary describing them—boom, clang, hiss, moan, pop, roar, squeak, and whir, as well as imitative noises such as ack-ack-ack and brr-brr-brrm. They should realize the importance of these sounds as communication, music, and noise. They should also begin to appreciate the effects of sounds on work, study, and relaxation, and the need for the control of sound as people and contrivances increase in number.

Finally, the exploration of vibrations and sounds is not only interesting and challenging in itself, but it can also contribute much to other important goals—competence in carrying out valid experiments and in making observations, proficiency in measuring and in keeping records, facility in working cooperatively with others, and, perhaps above all, a sense of accomplishment that comes from making a musical instrument, playing a scale or a song, or discovering how fast sound travels in air.

SOME IMPORTANT
OBJECTIVES

*ATTITUDES AND APPRECIATIONS
TO BE ENCOURAGED:*

Vibrations and sounds are important in our lives, and we should learn about them so that we can use and control them better.

Man learns about vibrations and sounds by performing experiments, making observations and measurements, keeping records, noting relationships, and testing ideas and hunches.

The nature and rate of vibrations depend upon definite and measurable factors, not on chance or the supernatural.

Even commonplace vibrations and sounds are interesting.

As people live and work more and more closely together and use more and more motors and machines, it becomes increasingly important to reduce undesirable sounds to a minimum.

Because not all people enjoy the same sounds, no one has the right to inflict sounds on others against their will.

The aesthetic enjoyment of music is important even though it may not lend itself to scientific study and measurement.

*SKILLS AND HABITS
TO BE DEVELOPED:*

Being aware of vibrations and sounds of various kinds in the environment and of differences among them

Discerning whether one sound is higher or lower than another, or of the same pitch, and comparing the loudness of sounds

Finding the rates of vibration of various objects by measurement and by comparison with objects of known vibration rates

Experimenting with vibrating objects to see, by measurement or by comparison, the effect of changing various factors

Predicting the effect that changes made in objects will have on their vibration rate or pitch

Making simple musical instruments using stretched strings, air columns, and pieces of wood, and playing scales and songs on them

Identifying the vibrating objects in musical instruments, the human voice, and other common sources of sounds

Employing objects as sounding boards to make sounds louder

Detecting echoes, and relating their delay to the distance of the reflecting surfaces that cause them

Using correctly such terms as air column, echo, frequency, octave, pitch, rate, sounding board, tautness, vibration, and xylophone

*FACTS AND PRINCIPLES
TO BE TAUGHT:*

Many objects vibrate, including pieces of wood and metal, stretched ropes and strings, air columns, and bodies of water.

Objects vibrate in various ways and at widely differing rates.

The rate of vibration of stretched ropes and strings depends, in part, on their tautness, while that of strips of wood and metal, as well as of air columns, is determined chiefly by length.

When vibrations occur rapidly enough, they produce sounds.

Most sounds we hear are produced when vibrating objects set the air to vibrating.

Many living things besides human beings communicate by means of sounds which, to us, are often unnoticed or inaudible.

Sounds differ in pitch, and this depends on their rate of vibration, or frequency.

Sounds can be made louder by setting larger surfaces into vibration.

Echoes are sounds that are reflected by objects; the farther the reflecting surface, the longer it takes an echo to return.

Sounds travel at a high, but measurable, speed in air.

TUNED TUBES

Pupils can have fun playing songs with the cardboard tubes from inside rolls of paper towels, waxed paper, and aluminum foil. While tuning them they can learn some of the basic principles on which wind instruments depend.

Ask pupils to bring such tubes from home. Let them tap them on their desks, or with pencils, and also blow across their ends. *Do they all have the same pitch? If not, what might cause this?*

Next, ask a few pupils with similar tubes to "play" them. Then let one cut 1/4 inch off his. *What does this do to its pitch?* Have another cut off 1/2 inch, and so on.

Now let each pupil shorten his tube, a little at a time, or lengthen it by taping on a piece, until its pitch matches a note on a piano or harmonica. When eight pupils have thus tuned their tubes to play a scale, ask them to give a concert!

Pupils may also carry on other investigations, as follows:

1. Hold two similar tubes together, end to end, and blow across one end. *How does their pitch compare with that of a single tube? The length of the air column with that inside a single tube?*

2. Find one tube that just fits inside another. Then "play" one while sliding the other in and out. *How does this affect the pitch? The length of the column of air? With what kind of band instrument is the pitch changed by sliding a tube in and out?*

3. *How does the pitch of a tube change when you close one end with your palm? Does this change the length of the air column?*

4. Let a stream of water fall noisily into a tall tumbler or jar. *What happens to the pitch of the sound as the water fills the vessel, causing the air column to become shorter?*

5. Collect eight pop bottles and, with seven friends, blow across their tops. Then tune the bottles by adding water.

MUSICAL DESKS

Violins, harps, pianos, and many other musical instruments have tightly stretched strings or wires which vibrate rapidly and produce sounds when they are bowed, plucked, or struck. These strings are tuned by making them more,

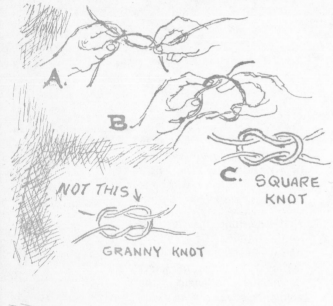

NOT THIS ↓

GRANNY KNOT

C. SQUARE KNOT

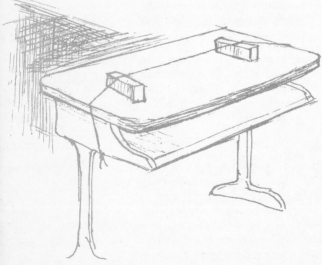

or less, taut. In some instruments the pitch of the strings is also changed while they are being played, by varying the length of the portions that vibrate. Usually the player does this with his fingers.

To make this information more meaningful to pupils, give each one a piece of *strong* heavy thread or thin string, long enough to go around the top of a desk or table, over and under. Help him to tie it *snugly* with a *square* knot and make it taut by slipping two narrow pieces of scrap wood between it and the desk or table top. Then let him pluck the raised portion and, if necessary, tighten it by raising the supports, so that it produces a clear tone. *How does its tautness affect the pitch of the sound?*

Some kinds of thread and string, including nylon fishline, hold their pitch rather well. With eight such strings, a team can make and tune an instrument on which to play songs. Or eight pupils may make their desks into one-note instruments, put them in a line, and play songs by plucking the strings as a "conductor" points to each one in the proper order. Sometimes the quality of the tone is improved by removing books, lunches, and baseball gloves from inside the instruments! (See "Louder Sounds.")

It is also instructive for pupils to:

1. Tap the strings lightly with a pencil.

2. Stroke them with a violin bow, fairly near one support.

3. Play a string while lifting one support slightly.

4. Pinch a string between two fingers while playing it.

5. Hold an ear to the desk while someone plays a string.

SHINGLE SONGS

With some scrap wood, thumb-tacks, and string, a class can make simple xylophones and thus learn about factors which determine pitch. The word *xylophone*, from the Greek, means "wood sound."

Cedar shingles, possibly scraps from new housing, work well. Split them with a knife into pieces about 1 inch wide. Give one to each pupil and let him saw a 5- to 8-inch length from its thick end. Coping saws work well and are safe. Show how to use them properly, on an old table or large crate. Other wood may also be used, such as narrow pieces from boxes, and lattice or furring strips from a lumber yard.

When several pupils have cut pieces, let them stand in line on a tile or concrete floor, in order of the length of their pieces. Then ask them to drop the pieces in turn, while everyone listens. *What, in general, happens to the pitch as the pieces get shorter? What might cause any exceptions?* Have pupils compare the width and thickness of the pieces, as well as their grain and denseness. Also let them split some of them further or saw them shorter.

At another time play a scale, slowly, on a piano or other instrument—even a harmonica. After each note have pupils drop pieces of wood until one of matching pitch is found. Then, when eight pupils have pieces that play a scale, let them make a xylophone by hanging the pieces on string. Two thumbtacks, with the string wrapped once around each, are driven into each piece, about a

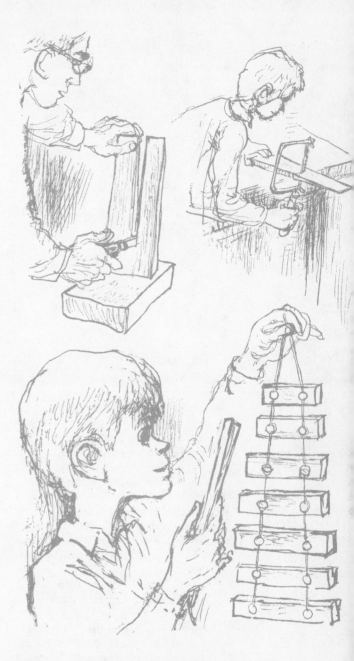

quarter of the way in from its ends. Then the finished instrument is played by tapping it with a stick.

Continue helping pupils select pieces, sawing them shorter when necessary, until everyone has made some contribution, even if out of tune! A scale requires eight pieces or more, but even four may sound a chord, such as C-E-G-C.

LOUDER SOUNDS

Pupils may observe that stringed instruments such as pianos and guitars can make louder sounds than those produced by strings around desks. (See "Musical Desks.") They can find out why this happens by using pocket combs and various objects in the classroom. With their hands, voices, and ears they can also learn other ways to make faint sounds louder and to hear them better.

First, show them how to hold a pocket comb in one hand and stroke its teeth with the thumb. Then let each one do this with his own comb. Next, divide the class into small groups and let each group compare the loudness of the sound made by stroking a comb, as indicated, with that made by stroking a comb while one end is held firmly against a desk. Have them try it against other objects, too, such as the teacher's desk, cupboard doors, blackboards, windows, waste baskets, oatmeal boxes, shelves, and even guitars.

Which of these things make the best sounding boards? Which are poorest? How does the bulletin board compare with the door? Does pressing a hand against a good sounding board change its effectiveness?

At another time ask a pupil to go to the front of the room and read aloud in a low voice. Let the rest listen, with their hands cupped behind their ears, then with them cupped in the opposite direction but in front of their ears. *When is the sound louder?* Now ask the reader to read from the back of the room. *How should the listeners, still facing front, hold their hands to hear best?*

Finally, ask the pupils to close their eyes while the reader continues in the back. From time to time signal him to cup his hands around his mouth, without pausing in his speech. *Does this make the sound louder? How should he hold his hands to make it fainter?* Let him do this, and then see if the class can hold their hands so as to compensate for the faintness of his voice.

BUZZ
RATES

Pupils may think of vibrating piano strings only as a way of producing musical notes, but they can also be used to tell how fast *other* things vibrate. For example, with the help of a piano, a pupil can tell how rapidly a mosquito's wings beat as it flies.

The pitch of a sound made by a vibrating object is a measure of its rate of vibration (or *frequency*). Objects which produce the same pitch vibrate at the same rate. On a properly tuned piano, the strings are adjusted to vibrate this many times each second:

middle C	262	F#	370
C#	277	G	392
D	294	G#	415
D#	311	A	440
E	330	A#	466
F	349	B	494

For each octave above one of these notes, the vibration rate is double; for each octave below, it is one-half. C above middle C, for ex-ample, has twice the rate of middle C, or about 524 vibrations per second. *What would it be for a note an octave above G?*

Ask your pupils to write down how rapidly they think a mosquito's wings vibrate as it flies. Then let each pupil try to find out for him-self, following these directions:

Catch a mosquito or other small flying insect and put it in a jar covered by a piece of cheesecloth or a handkerchief. Copy the above list of vibration rates. Then take both the list and the jar to a piano. Put your ear to the jar and listen to the insect's buzz, then pick out the note on the piano that most closely matches it. *According to the list, how rapid are the wingbeats of the mosquito? How rapid are the wing-beats of a housefly? A wasp?*

When a person sings, his vocal cords vibrate as air from his lungs moves past them. *What is the fast-est that you can make them vibrate? The slowest? How rapidly does the air vibrate when you whistle? What is the frequency of the highest reed on a harmonica?*

UNHEARD VIBRATIONS

Pupils commonly see objects vibrating back and forth, up and down, or side to side. Such vibrations are often desirable, as in clock pendulums, diving boards, and pogo sticks, but they may be unpleasant or dangerous, as when ships roll, suspension bridges swing, or buildings sway during earthquakes.

In this connection it is interesting for groups of pupils to investigate the vibrations of pieces of steel bands from around packing cases or lumber. Cut several straight pieces about 2 feet long, and give one to each group. Have them rest one end on a desk and weight it down with blocks or books set even with the edge of the desk. Then ask them to lift its free end and let go. *How many complete up-and-down vibrations does the strip make in one minute—or would it make if it continued to vibrate this long?* Let them check this carefully and keep a record.

Does the strip slow down as it vibrates? Suggest that the group compare the number of vibrations it makes during 10-second periods —at first, later on, and still later.

Now have them move the strip so that less of it extends beyond the desk. *What effect has this on its rate of vibration? How could the strip be used to measure time?* (See "Swinging Second-timer.")

Let them continue experimenting with the strip, varying the length of its vibrating part. Show them how to clamp the fixed end tightly by pressing a block of wood down on it, exactly even with the edge of the desk. Have them record the rate of vibration for each length and then make a bar graph by marking the various lengths along the bottom edge of a large sheet of cardboard or the chalkboard, and

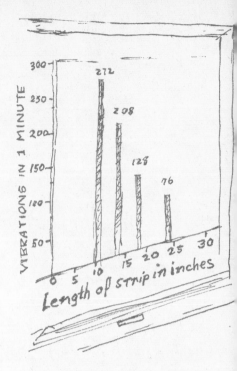

representing their rates of vibration by vertical bars.

As the vibrating portion of the strip is made shorter, do its vibrations, after a while, become too rapid to count? Does it eventually produce a hum or buzz? As it is shortened further, what happens to the pitch of the sound? (See "Buzz Rates.")

Pupils may also investigate other vibrations, as follows:

1. *Does the rate of vibration of parts of other objects also depend on their length?* Try yardsticks, plastic spoons, hacksaw blades, straightened-out bobby pins, and other things. *Do these objects also produce sound when they vibrate rapidly enough?*

2. Get a straight and uniform, narrow strip of scrap wood or a lattice strip, 10 or 12 feet long, from a lumber yard. Hold it in the middle, so that it balances, and make it spring up and down at its natural rate. *How many complete vibrations does it make in one*

minute? Check this and keep a record. Now saw off a 1-foot piece from one end of the strip, and again record the vibration rate. Saw off another foot, measure the rate, and so on. Make a graph to show how the vibration rate is related to the length. *How long is the strip when its vibrations are too rapid to count? What would you estimate the rate to be for a piece only 6 inches long?* To find out, cut off a 6-inch piece and drop it on a hard floor. (See "Shingle Songs" and "Buzz Rates.")

3. Tie the ends of a piece of shade cord or strong twine, about 30 feet long, to two chairs placed far enough apart to keep it taut. Have a pupil sit on each chair. Then pluck the cord at the center, sideways, and note its vibration. *What is the effect of tightening it even more? Might a very taut string vibrate so rapidly as to produce sound?* (See "Musical Desks.")

4. Fill a pan or basin with water. Place it so that you can see a bright reflection in the water. Now touch the water with a pencil point and note the ripples. Make a series of ripples by moving the pencil up and down rapidly. Then fill a can to the brim with water, tap its side, and listen to the sound it makes. Also look closely to see the tiny ripples. *How do the vibrations that cause them compare in rate with those of your pencil?*

5. Make a "chain" of four or more slender rubber bands, tie one end to a coat rack, and hang a paper cup on the other. Put pebbles, chalk, or large nails in the cup, pull it down a little way, and let go. *What happens? Does the amount of stuff in the cup affect how many up-and-down vibrations it makes in 10 seconds?* This also works well with a spring, such as an old shade spring, a "Slinky," or a hacksaw blade. (See "Saw-blade Balance.")

SOUND
BOUNCE

It is well known that an echo is caused by the reflection of sound by a building, cliff, or other large object, somewhat like the rebound of a rubber ball when it hits a wall. Sharp, distinct echoes are made by a large, plain outside wall of a building which faces an open field or play area, especially if there are no other large reflecting surfaces nearby. These echoes can give pupils excellent experiences with the speed of sound.

Take the class outdoors, a few hundred feet from the wall, when it is quiet and there is no wind. Ask one pupil to bang the bottom of a large can with a stick, while the rest listen for the echo from the wall. Then walk toward the wall together, and repeat this at various distances from it. *Is there a noticeable change in how quickly the echo returns?*

Pupils can find the approximate speed of sound in this way, using a "Swinging Second-timer." They should stand a few hundred feet from the wall, and observe carefully while one of them very regularly, after some practice, hits the can so that each bang occurs at the precise instant the pendulum is at one end of its path. *Then, is each echo heard at the exact time the pendulum reaches the opposite end of its path?* If not, they should change their distance from the wall until it *is* heard at this time. When each bang occurs just as the pendulum reaches one end of its swing and the echo is heard when it is at the opposite end, it means that the sound travels to the wall and back in the time the pendulum takes to make one-half of a complete swing —one-half second. *How far is it from the can to the wall and back?* (See "Wheel Measure.") The sound travels this far—to the wall and back—in one-half second. *How far, then, does it travel in one second?* This is the approximate speed of sound in air at the existing temperature.

leisurely learning

Learning in science should not be hurried. Children need time to mull ideas, discuss them with classmates, make observations, find additional examples, weigh evidence, think of alternative explanations, and test ideas in situations that seem applicable.

There seems to be increasing competition among schools and among children to cover a prescribed amount of subject matter in the elementary grades. Since elementary school pupils have at least six years of schooling ahead of them, including six years of science if they become interested, learning in science in the first six grades should be leisurely.

Pupils should have time to think about what they themselves do, not merely what they see others do. They also need time for doing things in groups where they must think critically and communicate with each other. They need time to practice and to master skills such as measuring, recording, and communicating, and to develop attitudes and appreciations as well. You, the teacher, must allow pupils time to brainstorm and to be creative, time to test their ideas in new situations, and time simply to enjoy science.

It may be frustrating to let a pupil flounder a bit in his search for knowledge and understanding, especially if you know or think you know the answer. Yet, as in a treasure hunt, much of the fun of learning lies in the search, not in the answer.

Just as a treasure hunt would be spoiled by giving away the secret, a child's imperfect attempt to find something out for himself may be spoiled by telling answers too quickly. When you are tempted to tell, remember that it is the process of science, not the answer, that is most important. Telling saves time, if you are more eager to save time than to open minds, but it is far better to let pupils explore thoroughly and learn leisurely. Then learnings will be more lasting and science more enjoyable.

magnetism
and
electricity

9

Daily life is truly dependent on magnetism and electricity. Youngsters meet applications of them on every hand—in toys, lights, stoves, refrigerators, television sets, and numerous other devices which provide the control of tremendous energy, a great deal of pleasure, and a degree of convenience too often taken for granted. When they become adults, these children will rely on magnetism and electricity, directly or indirectly, for their livelihood.

It seems obvious, therefore, that all pupils should learn the basic principles of magnetism and electricity. The subject is highly interesting to them, and it creates an enthusiasm for further study which, for some, may lead to a life's work. Moreover, it serves as a medium for other aspects of basic education, including arithmetic, oral and written communication, and manual skills—for girls as well as boys!

Much of the fascination of magnetism and electricity stems from their strangeness: ordinarily invisible in themselves, they can affect things at a distance—often without any discernible material connection. Their curious behavior has long prompted scientists to wonder about the nature of magnetism and electricity, and the resulting investigations have led to some of the most fundamental of scientific concepts—those concerning the structure of matter, the basis for chemical change, and the nature of radiation.

It is important that children learn to respect, yet not fear, electricity. They must be taught the hazards of fallen wires, of worn appliance cords, of poking things into sockets and outlets, and of lightning. At the same time, they should be made to feel confident that they can control electric currents safely and that they can experiment without harm with magnets, flashlight cells, and the electric charges that result from rubbing.

SOME IMPORTANT OBJECTIVES

ATTITUDES AND APPRECIATIONS TO BE ENCOURAGED:

Electricity in the wires and outlets usually found in homes and schools is too dangerous for experiments by children, but one or a few flashlight cells are safe for them to use.

Since electric transmission lines are very dangerous, one must never fly a kite near them, climb the poles or towers, go anywhere near fallen wires, or throw stones at the insulators.

Magnetism and electricity are fascinating to learn about and experiment with; an interest in them may lead to a life's work.

Man has learned to control and use magnetism and electricity, even though he does not completely understand their nature.

Scientists have learned, and still learn, about magnetism and electricity by doing experiments, making measurements, and suggesting and testing explanations of their observations.

Although magnetism and electricity act mysteriously at times, there is no reason to consider them to be supernatural.

Electricity, in itself, does not pollute air or water; for this reason, it probably will be used increasingly in place of fuels in vehicles and homes.

SKILLS AND HABITS TO BE DEVELOPED:

Investigating whether magnetism acts through various materials

Magnetizing a steel object by stroking it with a magnet or by winding a coil around it and connecting the coil in a circuit.

Making and using a simple compass to find magnetic direction

Determining whether an object is magnetized, and if so, where its north-seeking and south-seeking poles are located

Making valid comparisons of the strength of magnets and of electromagnets

Finding out whether an object has an electric charge, and if so, whether the charge is positive or negative

Connecting wires properly to one another and to cells, sockets, and switches, so that they make good contact

Constructing simple switches, sockets, and circuits

Testing materials for their ability to conduct electricity

Using correctly such terms as compass, electromagnet, insulator, magnetic north, negative charge, repulsion, south-seeking pole

FACTS AND PRINCIPLES TO BE TAUGHT:

An ordinary magnet has two different *poles, north-seeking* and *south-seeking,* named for what they do when the magnet can turn.

Magnetic poles of the same kind tend to repel each other, while unlike ones tend to attract; there is attraction between either kind and unmagnetized iron.

The earth is a huge magnet; it affects a small, freely turning magnet in a compass, causing it to take a consistent position.

Objects may possess *static charges* of electricity, or they may have electric charges flowing along them as *currents.*

An electric charge on an object is one of two kinds: *positive,* if the object tends to repel wool that has been rubbed on rubber, or *negative,* if it tends to repel the rubber.

Objects with similar electric charges tend to repel each other, and ones with unlike charges to attract; an object with a charge of either kind and an uncharged object tend to attract each other.

Some materials, called *conductors,* permit electricity to flow along them readily, while *nonconductors,* or *insulators,* do not.

A cell, or a battery of cells, causes electricity to flow in a circuit; a switch is used to open and close the circuit.

For an electric lamp to light, it must be part of a circuit.

When electricity flows along a wire or other conductor, the conductor acts like a magnet, even though it contains no iron.

BOBBY-PIN COMPASSES

Whenever possible, pupils should carry out science activities themselves and not merely look on. For example, demonstrating a magnetic compass is not nearly as valuable as letting *every* pupil make and use his own compass, as follows:

First spread apart the prongs of a bobby pin so that they are in a straight line, except for a small bend at the center. Then hold it by the bend, and stroke the bobby pin about 50 times on a strong magnet. Rub its entire length, from tip to tip, on *one* end of the magnet only, always in the same direction. Keep the other end of the magnet far away from it. The bobby pin should then be magnetized strongly enough to pick up a paper clip.

Next, tie a *single, thin* thread to the bobby pin at the bend. Hang it up so it can swing freely, at least a few feet away from iron objects, such as scissors, pipes, and metal desks. If necessary, slide the knot

sidewise, until the bobby pin hangs level.

Have the entire class hang up their magnetized bobby pins in this way, as far apart as possible. Then let each pupil stand up and extend his arms parallel to his bobby pin after it has come to rest. *Is there general conformity in direction?*

What happens when the bobby pins are spun around and then left alone? The tips that consistently point northward (in the direction of midday shadows) are said to be *north-seeking.* They may be marked with dabs of red nail polish or small paper stickers.

A compass like this works especially well outdoors—if it is shielded from wind. To do this, hang the magnetized bobby pin in a gallon jar or jug, and tie the thread to a stick across the top.

Will the compass work as well if the jar or jug is filled with water? Does the bobby pin then swing as much as before? This is why airplane and ship compasses are liquid-filled.

NAIL
ELECTROMAGNETS

Electromagnets are extremely important in modern life—for lifting iron objects, communicating by telephone and telegraph, making electric motors run, controlling remote switches, generating electric currents, and numerous other purposes.

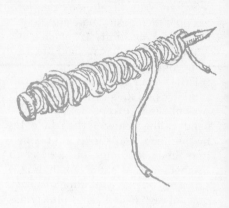

Even young pupils can learn about electromagnets and have the fun of making their own. They simply wind some insulated wire around a nail many times and touch the bared ends of the wire to a flashlight cell. The winding need not be neat. The cell, or even a few cells connected together, cannot give them a shock.

Caution pupils never to connect an electromagnet to an outlet!

Let each pupil make *his own* electromagnet. Give him a 3-inch nail and 8 to 10 feet of insulated copper wire. Have him wind all the wire around the nail, except for about 6 inches at each end. Help him to scrape the ends of the wire bare. Then let him hold one end tightly on the tip and the other against the bottom of a flashlight cell *briefly* and, at the same time, pick up paper clips, brads, or staples with the end of the nail.

Make sure pupils do not connect the electromagnets to the cells for more than a few seconds at a time. Otherwise the cells will soon become weak.

The best wire for this purpose is #20, 22, or 24 copper wire, insulated with plastic or cotton. Such wire is sold as *bell wire* and *magnet wire* by hardware and electrical supply stores.

If suitable wire is not available, or if a pupil wants to try something different, he may wind an electromagnet with a coil of aluminum foil, as follows: Cut a strip 2 inches wide and 12 to 14 feet long from a roll of household foil, and a similar strip, but 3 inches wide, from a roll of thin sheet plastic. Next, wrap a 3-inch nail in a single layer of foil so that the foil extends an inch or more beyond the point end. Then lay the aluminum strip lengthwise on top of the plastic strip and wind both of them tightly around the nail so that the plastic insulates each turn of the foil. Finally, tape the coil tightly and connect the ends of the foil to a flashlight cell.

Let pupils experiment with their electromagnets. *Are they as strong as ordinary magnets? Do they lose all their strength when disconnected? Can they act through plastic, aluminum, or rubber?*

Do electromagnets have two different poles like those of ordinary magnets? (See "Needle Poles.") *Does reversing the cell connections change their poles?* Let pupils check to see!

Later, after every pupil has made

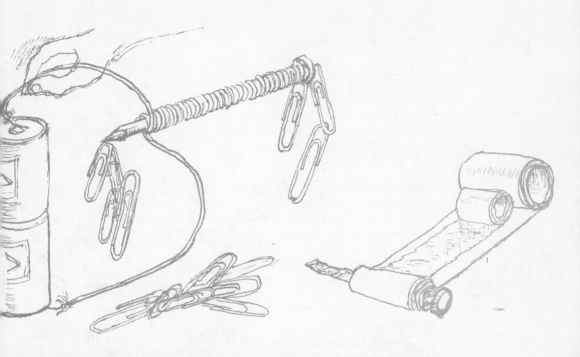

an electromagnet, let them have a contest to see who can construct the *strongest* one. Give them a choice of nails of many sizes and shapes and even some made of aluminum; wire of different thicknesses, lengths, and types of insulation; and not more than three flashlight cells. Let each design what he thinks will be the most powerful electromagnet he can make with these things and then construct it. Next, have everyone list on the chalkboard the number of paper clips his electromagnet can pick up at one time. (See if the pupils remember that nail electromagnets have *two* ends!) *Who has the strongest electromagnet in the class?*

Remind pupils never to connect electromagnets to cells for more than a few seconds at a time! The electromagnets weaken the cells quickly, and will ruin them if left connected.

A good way to compare the strength of two nail electromagnets is to place a paper clip between them, touching their heads. Then connect both electromagnets to the *same* cell at the same time, and pull them apart. Repeat this a few times. The one which holds on to the paper clip would seem to be the stronger. *Does the position of the paper clip make any difference?*

Through these experiences, pupils will come to realize that several factors affect an electromagnet's strength, including:

1. The number of turns of wire (or foil) in the coil

2. The length and thickness of the wire (or foil)

3. The number of cells connected together, end to end

4. The age of the cells and how much they have been used

5. The size of the core and the kind of metal in it

Some very large electromagnets are so strong that they can hold a man, upside down, by attracting the nails in his shoes!

NEEDLE POLES

After making "Bobby-pin Compasses," pupils can learn a basic principle of magnetism at first hand by experimenting with magnetized sewing needles. They should *all* participate in this way:

Hold a needle by its eye end and rub its entire length on *one* end of a strong magnet about 30 times, from the eye to the point *only*. Make a wide detour of the magnet on each return trip.

Next, set a bowl or an aluminum pan far from any iron or steel objects. Pour in some water and float on it a piece of aluminum foil as large as a quarter. Then lay the magnetized needle on the foil. *What does it do? If it is spun around, does it return to the same position each time? How does this position compare with that taken by the "Bobby-pin Compasses"?*

The end of the magnetized needle that points roughly northward is called the *north-seeking pole;* the other end is the *south-seeking pole.* Mark the north-seeking pole with some red nail polish or a small sticker. *Is it necessarily at the point end?*

Now take this needle off the foil, and magnetize another similar needle. Also find its north-seeking pole, and mark it. Then float one needle on the foil and, holding the other, bring it up close. *What do their north-seeking poles do when near each other? Their south-seeking poles? Two unlike poles? Do the poles of two magnetized bobby pins act in the same way? Of two magnetized hacksaw blades or coping-saw blades?*

A large, stationary steel object, such as a locker or cabinet, usually has magnetic poles. Pupils can locate and identify these poles by simply bringing a floating needle magnet very close to all parts of the object and noting which way the magnet points.

On the basis of what you have learned about how magnetic poles affect each other, would you say that the North Magnetic Pole of the earth is north-seeking or south-seeking? What effect has it on the north-seeking end of a compass?

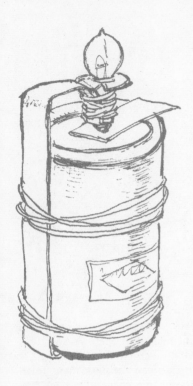

NIGHT LIGHTS

A good technique is to let pupils experiment, *with little or no direction,* to see if they can get a flashlight cell ("battery") to light a flashlight lamp ("bulb"). For this they may bring flashlight cells and lamps from home, as well as strips cut from thin aluminum pans, and odds and ends of wire. Ideally, *each* child should have his own cell and lamp, but pupils can take turns with fewer, if necessary. However, they should experiment *independently.* A demonstration would defeat the purpose!

Caution: Pupils cannot get shocks from flashlight cells, but be sure they stay away from electric outlets.

They are not likely to weaken the cells much, unless they connect top and bottom directly with a piece of metal. They will not "burn out" the lamps, except by connecting one to several cells at the same time.

How can a lamp be made to light? Can it be lit while held against the bottom of a cell? While not directly touching the cell at all? Can scissors be used to connect it? What else?

Afterward, each pupil may wish to make a night light for his bedside, in this manner: Using a rubber band or adhesive tape, fasten a flashlight lamp to one end of a 1/2-inch wide strip of stiff aluminum or a piece of fairly stiff bare wire, so that it makes good contact with the side of the base (see arrow). Or, if the lamp has a screw base, simply wind the wire in the grooves. Next, bend the strip or wire and fasten it to a flashlight cell with rubber bands or tape so that the bottom of the lamp (see arrow) makes good contact with the top of the cell. Then bend the strip or wire so that the bottom of the cell touches it when it is set down.

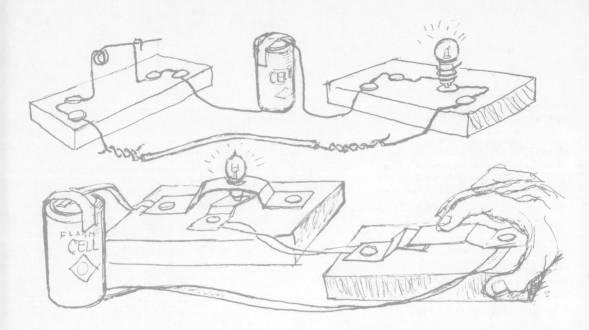

SOCKETS
AND
SWITCHES

An electric lamp ("bulb") lights when it is made part of a continuous loop of materials through which electricity flows. Such a loop is known as a *circuit*. A *socket* is just a convenient means of connecting the lamp in the circuit. A *switch* is simply an easy way to open the circuit and to complete it again, so that the lamp can be turned off and on.

Small switches and sockets for miniature lamps, such as flashlight lamps, may be purchased from science supply companies. However, they also can be made easily with thin aluminum (from pans and cans) or wire (preferably #18 or 20 copper "bell" wire, scraped bare), scrap pieces of soft wood, and thumbtacks.

A socket must hold a lamp firmly and at the same time touch its electrical contacts (see "Night Lights") with two pieces of metal which connect the lamp in the circuit.

A simple switch consists of two pieces of metal which, when touch-ing, close a gap in a circuit, and when released, open it and thus prevent electricity from flowing.

Pupils can make their own switches and sockets. Then they can connect simple circuits, using strips of aluminum foil or pieces of wire (#20, 22, or 24 copper wire is ideal), flashlight cells, and flashlight lamps. With these things they cannot get a shock.

Caution: Be certain that pupils stay away from electric outlets!

Then, by experimenting, they can answer questions like these:

1. *Can a circuit be connected with string or rubber bands?*

2. *Will a lamp light if the insulation is not scraped off the wires where they are connected? Must insulated wires be used?*

3. *Can a lamp be lit by connecting only one of its contacts?*

4. *Does it matter where the cell is located in a circuit?*

5. *Will a switch work equally well on either side of a lamp?*

CHARGED CHILDREN

It is generally known that some things, after being rubbed on wool, can attract threads, bits of paper, grains of puffed wheat, and other light objects. They are able to attract the objects, it is said, because they have a *charge of electricity*. Our word *electricity*, interestingly, comes from the Greek name for amber, *elektron,* which ancient peoples knew would attract bits of straw after having been rubbed with wool.

Pupils can easily produce electric charges on many common substances by rubbing two different kinds together. Some that work well are wool, plastic, leather, rubber, feathers, celluloid, brush bristles, and paper. They can be charged best when the humidity is low, as in a heated room during cold weather.

Children will be fascinated to find that they, too, can be given electric charges. To show this, ask a pupil wearing a *wool* sweater or jacket to stand on a short board resting on four cakes of paraffin. Then let someone rub his back briskly with a plastic raincoat, a large plastic bag, or an empty hot-water bottle.

If he becomes charged, he will be able to attract various light objects suspended by threads, including a balanced yardstick. He also can make a spark by touching someone's finger or a large metal object. In a dark room he will cause a bright flash in a fluorescent tube which someone holds for him to touch.

People often receive charges by sliding across plastic-covered car seats, scuffing their feet on rugs, or removing clothing made of certain

fabrics. They can then cause sparks, receive mild shocks, attract light objects, and make fluorescent tubes flash.

Can children wearing clothing other than wool be charged? How about synthetic fabrics? Plastic raincoats? Do they receive the same kind of charge in each case? (See "Kinds of Charges.")

KINDS
OF CHARGES

As a sequel to "Charged Children," it is worthwhile to explore with pupils the reasoning behind the recognition of two kinds of electric charges. Then they can test for these charges.

Lay two 6-inch lengths of *wool*

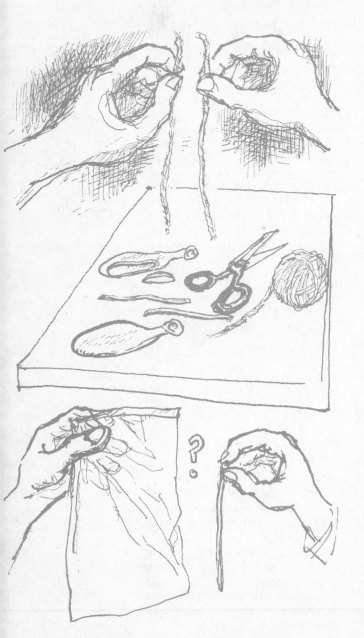

yarn on a desk and rub them lengthwise with a rubber balloon, several times. Then hold them up by one end, an inch or two apart. *What do they do?* Also try this with several pieces of yarn. These are samples of the *same* substance, and they have received the *same* treatment. *Is it not reasonable to suppose that they have the same kind of charge?*

Now cut two long, narrow strips of rubber from a balloon. Rub them with a ball of *wool* yarn, and hold them up near each other. *What happens?* These strips are alike, and they have been treated alike. *Does it not follow that they have the same kind of charge?*

Next, hold up a charged piece of wool near a charged strip of rubber. *Do they act like objects with the same kind of charge? What can one say, then, about the charges on them?* The charge on wool after it has been rubbed with rubber is arbitrarily called *positive;* that on the rubber, *negative.*

Investigations in which objects such as feathers, rubber bands, and strips of newspaper are rubbed with plastic, wool, silk, or other material show that samples of one substance often repel each other after they have been rubbed with another substance. If they do repel each other, they also repel either a charged piece of wool or a charged piece of rubber—never both. If they repel one, they attract the other. Those which repel charged wool have, as does the wool, a *positive* charge; those which repel charged rubber, a *negative* charge.

Knowing this, pupils can easily identify charges produced when different substances are rubbed together. They need only note whether a substance then repels charged wool or charged rubber.

PIE-PAN GENERATORS

When the air is dry, as in a heated room during cold weather, pupils often make sparks and get slight shocks when they touch a door-knob or other metal object after scuffing their feet on a rug. However, they can generate large electric charges and control them more easily with a pie-pan generator, as follows:

Stretch two rubber bands across a lightweight aluminum pie pan, at right angles to each other. Then flatten out a plastic bag on a desk, rub it briskly with *wool* cloth, and hold it up by one edge. Now lift the pan by the rubber bands, keeping your fingers away from the metal, and hold it against the bag. While it is in this position, touch the pan briefly with the tip of your little finger. *What do you hear?* Next, without touching the metal again, take the pan away from the bag and bring it to your nose. *What do you feel?*

It is fun to try this in a dark room or closet, and also to touch the charged pan to one end of a burned-out fluorescent tube which someone is holding by the other end. *What do you see?*

How a pie-pan generator works can be explained rather simply. When you rub the bag with wool, the plastic receives a negative electric charge. Then, when you hold the pan near the bag and touch the metal, this negative charge on the plastic causes negative electricity *in the metal* to be repelled from the pan to your finger, making a spark. As a consequence the pan is left with a positive charge. Finally, when you touch the pan to your nose, negative electricity jumps from you back to the metal, making a second spark. The kinds of charges on the plastic bag and the aluminum pan can easily be checked. (See "Kinds of Charges.")

An interesting variation is to use a flat piece of *wool* cloth or felt in place of the plastic bag and to rub it with plastic. *What kind of charge would you expect the pan to get now? Does it?*

CHARGES AND CURRENTS

It is often stated that electricity is of two kinds, *static* and *current*. This is somewhat like saying that there are two kinds of water, still and flowing. Experiments suggest that electricity, the *same* electricity, may be still (static), or flowing (current). Pupils can easily investigate this matter, as follows:

Rest a fluorescent tube (a burned-out one usually will work) on a table in a darkened room so that one metal end touches a large metal object, such as a locker, radiator, or pipe. Then produce an electric charge on an aluminum pie pan (see "Pie-pan Generators"), and touch the pan to the other metal end of the tube. *What does the tube do?* This works best when the air is dry, as in a heated room during cold weather.

Now fasten one bare end of a wire to this end of the tube, and run the wire through rubber bands held by a few pupils standing in a line. The wire should touch nothing but the rubber bands and the metal end of the tube. Charge the pie pan again, and touch it to the free end of the wire. *What does the tube show?*

As long as the electric charge stays on the pie pan, it is *static*. However, when the charged pan is touched to the wire, the tube flashes, suggesting that the charge flows from the pan to the wire, and along it to the tube. The motion of the charge constitutes a *current*. (Actually, electricity flows *from* the pan if it is charged negatively and *toward* it if it has a positive charge. The kind of charge on the pan depends on whether it is held next to charged wool or charged plastic when touched.)

How long can the wire be and still work? Can it be twice as long as the room? Do all kinds of wire work? Will string, thread, rubber bands linked together, or a strip of foil or of plastic serve in place of wire? Does wet *string conduct electricity?*

DETAILS ↑

Pupils rarely learn all they can from a single science experience. They may observe much of what happens. They may
even understand the principle involved. But learning to the
point of bringing about a change in behavior may result only
after repetition.

Some benefits that can accrue from repeated trials are:

1. Improved learning through reinforcement. In "Shadow
   Stick," pupils observe a shadow moving, but only after
   repeated experiences will most of them learn to predict
   within reasonable limits how far a shadow will move in
   an interval of time.

2. Greater validity of results. A class investigating "Seed
   Surplus" would not be able to make a valid judgment on
   the basis of one sample; therefore, many are taken
   and their combined results are used in arriving at a
   conclusion.

3. Greater awareness of details and subtle relationships.
   In "Taller or Wider?" pupils making their first measurement often completely overlook heels and hair, but
   these errors become obvious as they repeat their measurements using different subjects.

4. More opportunity to question, or to suggest new ideas.
   In "Masses and Motions," substitutions of objects or
   changes in position of and force on an object may lead
   to testing and modification of a hypothesis until it is
   accepted as correct.

5. Increased pleasure from the sheer fun of doing. In
   "Pie-pan Generators," pupils just are not satisfied with
   a once-only treatment. They like to see the sparks,
   hear the snap, and light a tube. Such pleasure is
   excellent motivation for learning.

"What would happen if . . .?" or "How would a change in
the weight affect . . .?" might be overheard as pupils try an
activity. Such questions are invitations to repeated trials.
The changing of one condition or the substitution of one
material for another in an investigation is good science and
should be encouraged.

light and
other
radiations

10

Visible light is without doubt one of the most important forms of energy. It is the major means of our learning about things and of communicating with others. It enables us to enjoy a landscape, a painting, and the starlit sky, and to photograph these things. It also enables a green plant to make food.

Early experiences with light should include playing with shadows, mirrors, and magnifiers. Children enjoy projecting fantastic figures on screens, using mirrors to see around corners, and peering through lenses at all sorts of things. They are intrigued by the magnifications, inversions, distortions, and other illusions they observe at water and glass surfaces.

In their study of light, pupils should become aware of the marvelous instrument their own eyes represent. They should find out how eyes are similar to, and different from, cameras and what constitutes proper care of the eyes. Experiments with color bring aesthetic pleasure, and can further their appreciation of the eye.

Practical applications of basic experiences with light should include practice in holding objects to avoid glare and annoying shadows. Pupils should also learn how to hold and use common optical instruments such as a hand magnifier, a microscope, a binocular, a camera, and a slide projector.

Important as it is, visible light is only a small part of a great family of radiations (or "waves") which travel easily through empty space. Invisible members of this family that can be studied by children are radiant heat and radio waves.

The sun's radiant heat is necessary for life on earth as we know it. Simple studies of this heat require only hand magnifiers and thermometers. The convenience and popularity of transistorized radios make possible experiments with radio waves, which are the most widely accepted means of long-distance communication.

SOME IMPORTANT OBJECTIVES

ATTITUDES AND APPRECIATIONS TO BE ENCOURAGED:

Human knowledge depends largely upon light, since direct observation is the basis for most of what we know about our universe.

Since we depend to so great an extent upon our ability to perceive light, our eyes should be given the best of care.

Just as some animals have a hearing range far beyond our own, there may be other animals or objects that are sensitive to radiations we cannot perceive.

Since most objects can be seen from many directions, space must be filled with light from a tremendous number of sources, traveling in an incredible number of directions.

Two persons' observations of a single event may differ because light, like any other sensation, must be received and interpreted, and no two persons will see the same thing in identical ways.

Seeing is not necessarily believing, since light can be bounced and bent to produce illusions not obvious to an observer.

Just as people differ in their sensitivity to sounds, they also differ in sensitivity to light, so that visual qualities such as color depend, in part, upon the person; they are not absolute.

What we see happening is always history, since light is not instantaneous, and the historical effect increases with distance.

SKILLS AND HABITS TO BE DEVELOPED:

Protecting one's eyes and those of others from injury and resisting the temptation to rub them if particles get into them

Determining the direction to light sources from observing the shadows cast by persons and other objects

Describing the form of an object from the shape of its shadow and predicting the shape of the shadow an object will cast

Manipulating two variables (such as a pencil *and* a screen) simultaneously to produce a desired result and then describing the degree to which each contributes to the result

Relating magnifying power to the degree of curvature of the surface of a lens or of a liquid-filled container

Making a magnifier from common materials such as water and wire

Holding and using to advantage instruments such as a magnifier

Predicting the field of view of a plane mirror and holding a mirror to send a beam in a desired direction or to see objects not in direct view

Recognizing a common element in two situations that produce the same result; e.g., that metal is common when both window screen and aluminum foil act as a barrier to radio waves

Using correctly such terms as transparent, light source, plane, reflect, convex, focus, radiation, and field of view

FACTS AND PRINCIPLES TO BE TAUGHT:

The closer an object is to a light source, the larger and less distinct is its shadow.

Straight lines are the directions in which light beams tend to travel.

Things seen through a convex (bulging) surface of a transparent solid or liquid usually appear magnified, but things seen through a concave (depressed) surface appear smaller than they really are.

The more sharply curved the surface of a magnifying lens, the greater is its magnifying power.

When a beam of light strikes a reflecting surface, the angle at which it leaves the reflector equals the angle at which it strikes.

A person looking at himself in a 10-inch upright mirror can see 20 inches of his image; in a 12-inch mirror, 24 inches; in a 14-inch mirror, 28 inches; and so on.

How much of other objects a person can see in a mirror depends upon where the objects, the person, and the mirror are in relation to each other.

Radio waves pass readily through glass, wood, plaster, and plastic, but not through metal, even when it has holes in it.

SHADOW SHAPES
AND SIZES

Young children love to pantomime animals with their fingers between a light source and a screen. As a teacher, you should capitalize on this interest to let pupils investigate what affects the size, shape, and sharpness of shadows.

With the help of the custodian, suspend a 200- or 300-watt lamp near the center of the room. See that each pupil has a pencil, a sheet of paper, and a cardboard on which to tape the paper to make a flat, stiff screen. Have available a supply of straight pins, some washers, and a few small wooden cubes or dice. Darken the room, turn on the lamp, and let the pupils proceed as follows:

Hold the pencil so that its shadow on the screen is the same size and shape as the pencil. Hold it so its shadow is a small, nearly round spot. (If finger shadows bother, stick a pin into the side of the pencil and use it as an almost shadowless handle.)

Now try holding the pencil so its shadow is shorter, but no wider,

than the pencil. *Are both ends of the pencil the same distance from the screen? Is one end of the shadow more distinct than the other? Can you hold the pencil so that its shadow is longer than the pencil, but no wider? What is the longest pencil shadow you can make? The widest?* Notice that inclining the screen, as well as the pencil, affects the size and shape of the shadow.

Hold the washer so that its shadow is nearly a circle. Hold it so that its shadow is a line about as long as the diameter of the washer. Try holding the screen and the washer to make a line shadow as long as the screen. *Is the shadow equally sharp at both ends? Can you hold the cube so that its shadow has more than six edges? Less than four? Can a rectangular solid have a shadow with five sides?*

At home, hold a pencil under a single fluorescent lamp. *How does the shadow of the pencil held parallel to the lamp compare with one made when the pencil is swung at right angles to it? Can you tell why?*

BIG FINGER

Olives usually are sold in glass containers with small diameters. To find out why, each pupil can bring one of these empty bottles to school and follow the directions below.

Fill the bottle three-quarters full with water. Stick one index finger in the water, and hold the other outside the bottle to compare. *How do the appearances of the two differ? Does the finger in the water appear larger when you hold it near the back of the bottle or near the front?*

Put a ruler in the bottle, or if the bottle is too narrow for a ruler, make marks an inch apart on a strip of paper and put it in the bottle. *Does the bottle make inches appear longer?* Cut two strips of notebook paper, one with lines running lengthwise and one with lines running across the strip. Put both in the bottle. *What happens to the spacing? What happens to the appearance of the squares on a strip of graph paper placed in the bottle?*

Now try these same activities with containers of larger diameter, such as peanut butter or mayonnaise jars. *In which is the appearance of objects changed most?*

Replace the jars with non-round containers such as toothbrush holders. *Does a pencil in a water-filled toothbrush container look wider through the sharply rounded side or the flattened side?*

Try the same objects in a clear shampoo tube whose top has been cut off to make the opening larger. Squeeze the tube and see what difference its shape makes in the appearance of things inside. *If you wanted to make objects in a bottle look as large as possible, in what kind of a bottle would you put them?*

Put several small objects such as a pebble, a button, an olive, and a stick in a slender bottle, fill it with water, and cap it tightly. Show it to your pupils and see if they can tell the *real* size of each object without opening the bottle.

LITTLE FINGER

In "Big Finger" you learned how to make things look wider by putting them in a slender, round bottle filled with water. *What do you think would happen if the air outside the bottle and the water inside it were exchanged? (If a water-filled bottle in air makes things look wider, will an air-filled bottle in water make things look narrower?)* Let the children write their guesses, and then let them check their guesses by experimenting as follows:

Stand a clean, dry olive bottle on the bottom of an empty aquarium (or wide-mouth gallon jar) and hold it there while a partner pours water into the aquarium until the water level is just below the mouth of the bottle. Stick a finger down inside the bottle and, at the same time, hold the corresponding finger of the other hand in the water beside it. Ask your partner to ob-serve and compare the two fingers. *Does either finger appear magnified? Which one appears smaller? Where does the appearance of the finger inside the bottle change most —near the front of the bottle, or near the back?*

Try some other objects in the air-filled bottle. *Does the spacing of inch marks on a ruler or on a strip of paper seem to change inside the bottle?* Put a strip of squared paper in the bottle. *How does the apparent shape of graph-paper squares compare with what you saw in a water-filled bottle?*

Replace the slender olive bottle with a jar of larger diameter. Try your finger, a ruler, a strip of graph paper, and some other objects in it. *Can you see that things are not reduced in width so much as in the olive bottle?* Just as large-diameter jars filled with water do not magnify so much as small-diameter jars, large-diameter jars filled with air do not make things appear so narrow as do small-diameter jars.

WATER-DROP MAGNIFIERS

Pupils can feel that a magnifying glass is thicker at its center than at its edge. But they may not know what makes some magnifiers stronger than others. Given the following directions, however, they can find out for themselves:

DETAIL ENLARGED

Lay a book on a table and put a sheet of waxed paper over one of its pages. With a medicine dropper, put a drop of water on the waxed paper. Slide the paper on the page until the drop comes over a letter. *What does the drop do to the letter? Can you see the whole letter at once in the drop?*

An inch or so from the drop, make a larger water *lens* by putting five drops in a puddle. Slide the waxed paper until the puddle is over the letter you just looked at. *Does the puddle magnify the letter more or less than the single drop did?*

Make a puddle of 10 drops or more. Move this over the same letter and compare what you see now with what you saw before. *Which of the three lenses is strongest? Which lens lets you see more of the letter or word at a time? Do you think a lens can be a strong magnifier and let you see a large area at the same time?*

Bend down so that your eyes are almost at the level of the waxed paper and look at the three water lenses from the side. Compare the curvature (roundness) of the single drop with that of the two puddles. *Which has the sharpest curvature?* This is like the sharper curvature of a slender olive jar (see "Big Finger") compared with that of larger jars.

Bend the end of a wire around a large nail to make a loop. Catch a drop of water in this loop, hold it horizontally near a letter, and observe the letter. Carefully touch the drop with a finger and remove a little of the water from it. *What happens to the magnifying power of the water lens as it becomes thinner? Can you remove enough water to make it a reducing lens?*

SURPRISE
IN A MIRROR

Children, and even adults, who look at themselves in a mirror usually know *what* they will see, but not *how much.* A surprise is in store for both a teacher and class who experiment to find out.

Hold an inexpensive 8- by 10-inch rectangular mirror in front of a class and ask how much of themselves they think they could see in such a mirror. Have each pupil write his answer at the top of a paper, and following it, what he finds out by experimenting.

Divide the class into groups, each with a mirror similar to the first one. Have one pupil in each group hold the mirror flat against a wall. Let each pupil, in turn, stand where he can see himself in the mirror. At his direction, the mirror should be moved up or down until the top of his reflection is even with the top of the mirror. *How far down can you see? To your chin? Neck? Waist? Toes? Can you see more of yourself if you move farther away from the mirror? What if you move closer?*

Have each pupil measure on his person the amount of himself that he sees, and compare this with the length of the mirror. *How long a mirror does a person need to see his entire self?*

Let the pupils check this by drawing a figure of a person on a sheet of paper, punching a hole through one eye of the figure. Have each pupil, in turn, face a mirror, hold his drawing vertical, and look through the hole at his figure's reflection. Another pupil can mark where the reflection comes in the mirror. *How does the amount of mirror needed compare with the size of the figure? Does this support the conclusion about a full-length mirror?*

To show why this is true, ask each pupil to sketch a figure along the left margin of a sheet of paper. Pretend the right margin is a mirror. *How should a line be drawn to represent light from the top of the head being reflected to the eye? From the foot to the eye?* Notice that the mirror need be only *half* as long as the figure, regardless of the width of the paper.

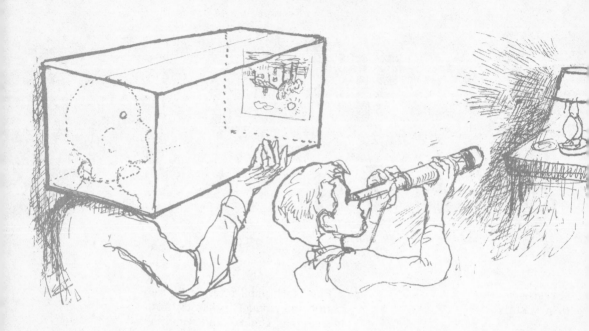

PINHOLE PICTURES

Before the days of photography, people sometimes entertained themselves by sitting inside a special dark room (the Latin word for room is *camera*) which had a small hole in its outer wall. The only light in the *camera* came from outdoors, through this hole. On a bright day this light produced a colored, moving picture of the outdoor scene on the wall opposite the hole, to the amusement of those inside. Sometimes a tentlike *camera* was set up outdoors in order to observe the sun, eclipses, or bright stars.

It is easy to make a small camera like this for younger pupils to use and enjoy, or as a model for older pupils to copy. Find a large cardboard carton that has not been torn and paste a sheet of white paper inside it against one end. Then tape the carton completely shut. In

the bottom of the carton, near the end opposite the paper and to the left of the center line, cut a hole just big enough to admit a pupil's head so that he can put his head inside the carton and look toward the paper. Then, with a large nail, poke a hole through the end of the carton, slightly above and to the right of where the pupil's head will be.

Now, when a pupil places his head inside the carton and stands so that the nail hole is pointed toward a bright window, a lighted lamp, or a sunlit outdoor scene, he can see a faint but fairly clear picture on the paper. *How does this picture compare with the actual scene in position? In color? In size? What happens to the brightness of the picture when the hole is made larger? To the sharpness?*

Let pupils go outdoors on a day when it is mostly sunny, but when there are some scattered clouds, and take turns pointing the nail the edge of the cardboard. Trim off any excess paper or plastic.

Slip the smaller tube inside the larger, keeping the open ends toward you. Hold one eye against the open end of the smaller tube, close the other eye, and point the pinhole toward a bright object such as a sunlit outdoor scene, a window, or an electric light. *Can you see a picture on the translucent screen? Is it black-and-white or colored? Right side up or upside down? Smaller or larger than the object itself? Does the image of a person walking past a window move in the same direction as the person does?*

Keep looking into the inner tube and slowly pull it out of the larger one. Then slide it back in. *As this is done, what happens to the size of the image? To its brightness?*

Now prick a second hole in the foil, 1/2 inch from the first. *What effect does it have on the image?* Rotate the outer tube and watch the image. Then enlarge one hole with a pencil point. *What does this do to the brightness of the image? To its sharpness?* Enlarge this hole still more, and note the effect.

Finally, replace the aluminum foil on the outer tube with a piece of *clear* sheet plastic, or fasten the plastic on another, similar tube. Make a tiny dot, preferably with India ink, at the center of the plastic. Then slip the smaller tube inside the larger and look into it as before. Observe the shadow cast by the dot when the tubes are pointed toward a lighted candle or a distant electric light. *How does it compare with the shadow cast when they are pointed at a bright window? What is the shadow like when the light comes from two candles?* Since the dot *stops* light instead of letting it pass, it acts as a "negative" pinhole.

hole toward the sun. *How big is the sun's image on the paper? What happens to the image when a cloud passes? Does the image of the cloud move in the same direction as the cloud does?*

Pupils can investigate pictures formed by light passing through a pinhole by making and using a still smaller camera, as follows: Find two cardboard tubes 1 1/2 inches or so in diameter and 10 to 12 inches long, one of them just able to slip inside the other. Mailing tubes or tubes from inside rolls of paper towels, aluminum foil, or waxed paper work well. Place a piece of aluminum foil across one end of the wider tube and tape it in place. Then make a pinhole in the center of the foil.

Close one end of the smaller tube with a piece of waxed paper, translucent ("frosty") plastic, tracing paper, or onion skin paper, taping it so that it lies flat, or fastening it with household cement spread on

SPACE SIGNALS

Radio waves are an important medium for communication in space. Even though they are invisible, there are some things pupils can learn about them. Ask the class to bring in one or more pocket-size transistor radios. Set one on a table where all can see and hear it. The radio station is some distance away, yet the waves it sends out are able to reach the radio. *Do they really pass through materials such as glass and plaster to do so? If other materials were used for windows and walls, would the radio still play?* Divide the class into as many groups as there are radios, and then let them experiment to find out, as follows:

Turn the radio on and set it inside a wide-mouth gallon jar. Cover the jar with a pane of glass, or invert another jar over the opening of the first. *Does the radio still play?*

To find out if radio waves will pass through water, put the radio (still turned on) in a plastic bag that has been checked for leaks. *(How would you check it for leaks without getting it wet inside?) Can you still hear the radio?* If so, immerse the sealed radio in a gallon jar of water and listen carefully. *Do radio waves still reach the radio? How can you tell?*

Remove the radio and wrap it in a large piece of aluminum foil. *What happens as the foil encloses the radio?* Open the foil to make sure the radio still is turned on, and then close it again. *Does the sound stop?* Cut a 1-inch hole in the foil. *Does the sound come out? What happens as you increase the number of holes?* Remove the foil completely. *What difference does it make? If you lower the radio into a metal pail, does it continue to play?*

By completely surrounding the radio with various materials, you can find out which ones block radio waves and which do not. Try window screen, rubber, cardboard cartons, and metal cans. *Why does a car radio need an antenna, although a house radio does not?*

**discovery
through
experiment**

The real essence of science is honest inquiry. Scientists discover new things because they inquire constantly into the unknown. Children, too, can discover by inquiring and experimenting. The things they find out may not be new or startling to you, the teacher, but to them even small discoveries are exciting.

Many so-called experiments are not experiments at all. Instead, they are verifications of something both teachers and pupils may know. Even so, they may be advantageous for learning, just as repeated trials are desirable. But discovery through experiment is one of the best means of developing:

1. The confidence that comes by finding out for oneself

2. A willingness to try new things, even though the procedures are unfamiliar and the outcome uncertain

3. An open-mindedness that ensures acceptance of a new idea if it proves to be more valid than a former one

The most effective experiments often are those which arise from pupils' own questions instead of from a textbook's or a teacher's suggestions. They motivate pupils much more than artificially imposed experiments and lead to purposeful and hence more efficient pupil activity.

Children's discoveries do not always agree with what others have found. Nevertheless, their discoveries are real, and should be considered "true" until a situation arises or can be arranged where repetition fails to verify their original findings.

When this happens, pupils' changes of mind should come from their own observations, not from adult authority. Scientists do not have a higher authority whom they can ask if their experiment "worked." Like scientists, pupils should learn to rely on what they discover through experiment, not primarily on what the teacher or book says. Their final authority should be the answer to, "What does Nature have to say?"

133

heat
and
temperature

11

All living things are dependent upon heat, but human beings have become skilled at controlling it and have developed conveniences such as refrigerators, push-button stoves, and thermostats in schools and homes. Children who enjoy such conveniences may not be aware of this dependence, and need firsthand experiences to understand fully some factors affecting the production and movement of heat, and the effect of temperature changes on various objects.

Basic experiences should include investigations of hot and cold objects and practice in measuring their temperatures; of how materials vary in their ability to conduct heat; and of some common sources of heat such as friction, electric currents, burning, and chemical action where there is no fire. They should learn to respect, but not to fear, heat sources and to use them safely.

Pupils should learn that the amount of heat in an object rarely remains the same for long, but is ever being added to or lost. The rate of addition or loss of heat can be controlled, however, and they should learn ways of doing it and be able to select and arrange materials for the purpose.

They should learn the difference between heat and temperature, that one is related to the kind and amount of stuff in an object and the other is merely an indication of how hot it is. They should learn, too, that cold is the absence of heat and that an object feels cold only as heat moves into it from one's body.

By learning about heat and temperature, children will apply understanding to keeping food hot or cold, to dressing comfortably, and to holding hot or cold objects without discomfort, as well as to appreciating the extremes of the environment to which other living things are subjected.

SOME IMPORTANT OBJECTIVES

ATTITUDES AND APPRECIATIONS TO BE ENCOURAGED:

Without energy from the sun to produce heat on earth, life as we know it would be impossible.

Man is not at the direct mercy of the weather because he has learned to insulate his body and his food and to control the temperature of his buildings.

Many other animals must endure extremes of temperature not noticed by man because of his clothing and his temperature-controlled homes, factories, and schools.

Conveniences such as refrigerators and stoves are so generally a part of our life that we tend to forget how dependent upon them we really are—until a power failure makes it clear.

Some people in our own country and millions in other countries still have only relatively primitive means of heating homes and cooking and thus endure hardships unknown to the rest of us.

Touch, including the use of feet, arms, and face, is not a very reliable way of sensing the temperature of different objects; it confuses temperature and conductivity.

Heat is an unavoidable by-product, often unwanted and wasted, of most energy transformations such as from electrical energy to light.

SKILLS AND HABITS TO BE DEVELOPED:

Reading a thermometer to a single scale division

Using matches properly

Selecting suitable nonconductors of heat with which to hold and support hot or cold objects or to keep food hot or cold

Exercising care not to leave in direct sunlight objects that might be harmed by the absorption of radiant energy

Using friction as a source of heat when needed, such as striking a match or rubbing hands together to get them warm

Opening a window slightly when a car is parked in sunlight

Avoiding waste of hot water, as in baths and showers, because of the unusually great amount of heat needed to make it hot

Remembering to allow room for expansion of liquids in containers, such as gasoline in a tank, in case they expand as they warm

Setting out containers of water to minimize changes in temperature, such as in a homemade incubator

Using correctly terms such as temperature, heat, radiant energy, absorb, heat conductor, heat insulator, expand, and mass

FACTS AND PRINCIPLES TO BE TAUGHT:

Most objects tend to expand when heated and contract when cooled, the extent depending on their dimensions, the material in them, and the temperature change.

Radiant energy from the sun is absorbed at different rates by objects which differ in color, composition, or angle to the sun.

When water absorbs or loses a certain amount of heat, it changes temperature less than almost any other substance.

Metals conduct heat well, but most other substances—including glass, wood, plastic, porcelain, paper, fur, and fabrics—do not.

Dark-colored objects in sunlight often tend to become warm, sometimes even very hot, but light-colored objects usually remain relatively cool.

Heat is not static; it is transferred continually from warmer to cooler objects.

Steel bridges, large buildings,

some engine parts, and long pipes have provisions for allowing them to expand and contract with temperature changes; sometimes they creak as they do so.

A large quantity of a substance has more heat than a smaller amount at the same temperature; it may still have more heat even if the smaller amount is warmer.

Whenever heat is lost by one object, it is gained by another.

HEAT TRAPS

In addition to light that we see, the sun gives off other forms of radiation. Some of this raises the temperature of surfaces that it strikes; hence, it is commonly called "heat radiation," even though it has no temperature until it is absorbed. To show how various surfaces differ in their ability to absorb this radiation, take your pupils to a nearby parking lot on a warm day to investigate the temperature of cars that stand in the sun.

Ask each pupil to feel the top of the hood of a light-colored car. Then let them try the hoods of black or dark-colored cars. *Is there a noticeable difference?* Now have them test cars of a variety of colors. *How do their temperatures compare, according to the touch test? Does the position of the surface with respect to the sun's rays make a difference?*

Then get permission to place thermometers on the seats of both light- and dark-colored cars. Leave them for a half hour. Be sure that the windows are closed, and that the thermometers are not in direct sunlight, or they will not indicate the air temperature. Have the pupils read the thermometers as soon as the doors are opened. *In which cars is the air hottest? How hot?*

On another warm, sunny day take your class to a place where a blacktop drive meets a concrete walk. Let pupils who wish to do so remove their shoes and stand on the blacktop, then on the concrete. *Is the concrete warmer or cooler than the blacktop? How does this difference compare with observations made in the parking lot?*

Since dark-colored objects ordinarily are better radiant-heat absorbers than light-colored ones, snow usually melts on blacktop roads more quickly than on concrete ones. *If you lived in the tropics where there was no snow, would you prefer a light-colored or a dark-colored roof on your house? Why?*

ICE-MELTING CONTEST

Children often use special containers for keeping things hot or cold by retarding the flow of heat to or from them. To understand some ways in which the insulation is accomplished, they can have a contest, using ice cubes, that is both fun and instructional.

First, let the pupils pair off and go outdoors. Give each team an ice cube of equal size. At a signal, let them play "melt the cube," each team bringing heat to its cube by any means except smashing the cube or applying artificial heat. One pupil, or you the teacher, should act as timer. The first team to melt its cube completely wins the game. Afterward, return to the classroom to discuss the results.

How many used the heat of their bodies to melt their ice? How many rubbed their hands to warm them before holding the ice cube, or rubbed the ice directly on their clothing? Did any think to use dark (and hence often warm) *objects?* (See "Heat Traps.") *What procedure proved most effective?* When the pupils have exchanged observations, let them run the contest again to see how much improvement each team can make over its first try.

At another time, let the pupils propose ways to *prevent* the melting of an ice cube by the use of materials such as paper towels, aluminum foil, cloth, and cardboard. Let each team write down what they think would be the best way, then let them test their ideas in another contest—a "preserve the cube" contest. *Can any team keep its cube for an entire school day, without taking it out of the classroom? What material, or combination of materials, proves to be the best insulator?* See if the pupils can tell why.

Finally, let the class investigate the kinds of insulation used in containers such as insulated bags, plastic coffee cups, and discarded picnic jugs. *What is the purpose of each material?*

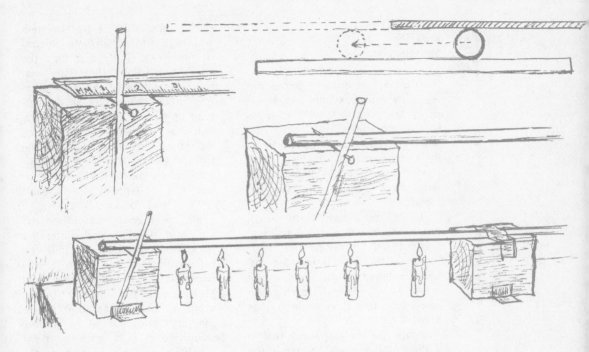

CURTAIN-ROD
BRIDGE

Metal bridges expand and contract as their temperature changes. They usually are set on rollers to allow for this. What takes place may be shown with a model bridge made from a discarded metal curtain rod that is a few feet long and straight.

Support its ends on two similar smooth wooden blocks set on a table and taped in place so that they will not slide. Tape one end of the "bridge" firmly to one "pier". Then stick a pin through the middle of a shortened drinking straw to serve as a pointer, set it on the other "pier," and rest that end of the "bridge" on it.

Set several short candles under the "bridge" and light them. *What happens to the pointer? Why is this? What will it do if the flames are put out? If snow or crushed ice is sprinkled gently on the "bridge"?* Let pupils check to see.

Bridges, of course, are not usually heated by fires. To show the effect of more normal tempera-ture changes, glue the "piers" to a length of two-by-four, set up the "bridge" without candles, and carefully take it outdoors on a cold day. Later bring it in.

The pointer shows how much the "bridge" changes in length. One full turn would indicate a change equal to *twice* the circumference of the pin. To make this clear, roll a stick across a cardboard tube on a table, measure how far the *stick* moves when the tube makes one turn, and compare this distance with that around the tube. To find the circumference of the pin, roll a centimeter ruler across it as it lies on the block with the pointer over the edge, note how far the ruler moves *with respect to the pin* when the pointer makes 10 turns, and divide this distance by 10.

On the basis of these tests with one metal rod, is it valid to say, "Metals expand when heated?" What should one do before making such a sweeping generalization? What can you conclude from the evidence you have?

SHRINKING AND SWELLING AIR

In "Curtain-rod Bridge," pupils can see how much certain metals expand and contract with changes in temperature. By observing what happens to air samples as their temperature changes, they can compare the changes in gases with those changes observed in metals.

Divide the class into small groups, each with a round balloon, a quart jar, an inexpensive thermometer that fits inside the jar, some rubber bands, and several feet of string. Then let each group investigate the changes in air, as follows:

Inflate the balloon and seal it with a rubber band. *What is the approximate temperature of the air inside?* Now find the distance around the middle of the balloon and record it, either by marking the string or by measuring its length. Then set the balloon where it is much warmer or much colder than when it was inflated, and leave it for a half hour. Record its temperature. (By that time the air in the balloon should be near the temperature of the air around it.) Holding the string on the balloon *at the same place as before,* measure and record the distance around the balloon. *How has the balloon changed in size? Approximately how much did it change in temperature? Is this change greater or less than for metals?*

Put the thermometer inside the jar. Cut the half containing the neck from the balloon, pull the rest of the rubber down tightly over the top of the jar, and hold it in place with rubber bands. *What is the temperature inside the jar?* Cool the jar by putting it outside or in a refrigerator for a half hour. *What happens to the rubber as the temperature inside the jar changes? Where could the jar be placed to make the rubber cover bulge up?* Try it! But when you do, remember to record both the temperature inside the jar and the shape of the cover.

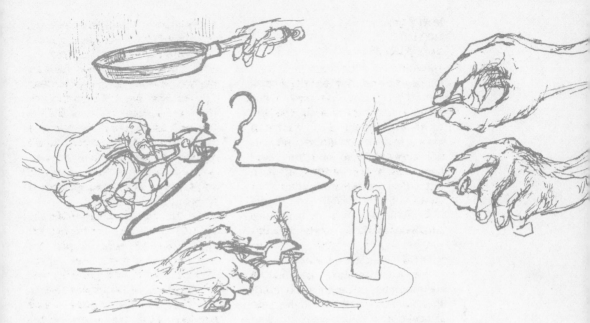

HEAT
RACES

Sometimes it is an advantage when heat travels quickly through a substance, as through the bottom of a pot on a stove, while in other instances, as in the handle of the pot, it is better if it travels slowly. Pupils can learn at first hand which of some common materials are good conductors of heat and which are not.

Divide the class into groups of about five. Appoint a "Candle Caretaker" in each group to set a candle securely in a metal pan, light it safely, and be responsible for it.

Caution: He should have a can of water at hand in case of emergency.

Then give each group a 3-inch piece of iron wire, such as coathanger wire, and an equal length of copper wire of the same diameter, such as scrap electric wire with the insulation removed. *Which is the better conductor of heat?* Let each pupil, in turn, find out by holding one end of both

wires with their other ends in the candle flame. Ask them to record their observations, but not to share them with anyone until *all* have tested the wires.

In the same manner, let pupils test other matched pairs of wires, such as aluminum and iron, or aluminum and copper, as well as narrow strips of various kinds of sheet metal. Suitable wires and strips can be obtained from electric shops, hardware stores, sheet metal shops, and junkyards, or from pupils' fathers.

Pupils can also compare the heat conductivity of wood with that of iron by holding a matchstick and a nail of the same size in the flame. Likewise, they may test the conductivity of a piece of glass rod obtained from a high school science department. *How do these three materials rank in order of heat conductivity?*

After all pupils have recorded their observations, let them see if they agree on the order of conductivity of all the substances tested. *Which is the best conductor? The poorest? Of what practical value are these facts?*

HEAT
MIXTURES

The difference between heat and temperature is not clearly understood by many persons. They understand the meaning of the word *hot*, and they know what it means to *heat* something, but it is not clear to them how one container of *warm* water can have more heat in it than another container of *hot* water. A simple investigation with water mixtures will help to show pupils how this can be.

Divide the class into four groups, giving each group a laboratory thermometer or a cheap outdoor thermometer with a thin (and hence not massive) scale attached to the glass, three 8-ounce and one 16-ounce styrofoam hot drink cups, and a clean quart milk carton whose top has been cut away. At opposite sides of the room place three plastic pails of water—one cold, one warm, and one hot but not scalding. Then let each group proceed as follows, with each pupil making and recording his own observations:

Fill one small cup three-quarters full with cold water. Make a pencil mark on the cup at the water level, and pour the water into a second cup. Mark where the water level comes, and pour the water into a third cup. Again, mark the water level. Now there are marks on all three cups to indicate equal measures of water. One cup still holds cold water.

Fill a second cup to its mark with warm water. Take the temperature of the water in both cups. Now, without showing it to others, write your prediction of what the temperature will be if both cups of water are mixed in the large cup. When all have written their predictions, try it and see. *How does the temperature of the mix-*

ture compare with the temperature in the cold and warm cups? How close was your prediction to the actual result?

Pour out the mixture and try it once more, this time using samples of cold and hot water. Record their temperatures, write your prediction about the temperature of the mixture, then test to find out. *How does the temperature of the mixture compare with that of the samples? How close was your prediction? Can you see that when equal masses of water are mixed, the temperature of the mixture is midway between the temperatures of the masses?* One is just as effective as the other in determining the result.

Now put two measures of hot water in the large styrofoam cup and one measure of cold water in a small one. Take their temperatures, record them, and write what you think will be the temperature of the mixture. Then pour them into the quart carton and find out for yourself. *How does the tem-*

perature of the mixture compare with what you observed in the cups? How close was your prediction?

Repeat the activity, using two measures of cold water mixed with one of hot water. *Can you see that the temperature of the mixture depends not only upon the temperature of the separate samples, but upon their masses?* A mass of water twice as great as another is twice as effective in determining the final temperature.

To test pupils' understanding of this principle and to demonstrate that a large mass of water, even though cooler, can have more heat than a smaller mass, fill an 8-ounce styrofoam cup with water at 120°F, and a 16-ounce one with water at 110°F. Then fill two 8-ounce cups with water at about 40°F. (To get water at this temperature, stir some ice in a quart of water until the water is at the desired temperature, remove the ice, and fill the two cups.)

Let two pupils check the tem-

perature of the water in a cold cup and in the smaller hot one, and when they agree on the temperatures, write them on the board. Next, ask each one in the class to write down his prediction of the temperature when the two cups of water are mixed. Pour the two into a quart container and let the same two pupils check the temperature. *How many of the class predicted it within 3 degrees?*

Now ask what will happen when the larger, but cooler (by 10 degrees), cup of water is mixed with the remaining cold one. Again, let two pupils check the temperatures and record them. Mix the two masses of water and then let the same pupils observe and announce the temperature of the mixture. *How many predicted it within 3 degrees? Which mass of water—the smaller, hot one, or the larger, but cooler, one—produced the warmer mixture?* Let the pupils who came closest in their predictions explain how they figured this out.

PAPER BOILER

Most children know that paper and cardboard will burn when held in a flame. But they may not know that each material must be raised to a particular temperature before it will ignite and that for paper this temperature is considerably higher than the temperature of boiling water. It amazes them to observe that water can be heated to boiling over an open flame in a paper "boiler" without the paper itself burning.

Provide each group of about five pupils with a metal pie pan, a 5- by 7-inch sheet of paper, a 5-inch square of window screen, a large juice or soup can whose top and bottom have been removed, and a stout candle 1 inch shorter than the can. Several draft holes should be made at one end of the can with a punch-type opener. Then have each group drip wax in its pan and set the candle upright in it.

To make the boiler, the paper should be folded 1 1/2 inches from each edge, the squares at each corner folded diagonally, and the sides wrapped around the ends and held with a paper clip as shown. Water should be added to a depth of not more than 1/2 inch. Then the candle should be lighted, the can set over it with the draft holes at the bottom, the screen laid across the open top, and the boiler with its water placed on the screen.

Have the pupils test the water temperature with their fingertips at the end of each minute. *Does the boiler show any signs of burning?* (Sooty deposits from the candle do not mean charring of the paper.) *Whose boiler is the first to show bubbles forming at the bottom? Whose is the first to "steam?"*

So long as there is water in the boiler, the candle flame cannot heat the paper to its *kindling temperature.* The water limits the temperature to which the flame can raise the paper, even though heat is added to the container and its contents.

Caution: This should not be tried on a kitchen stove. Too much heat can be dangerous.

keeping
records

"Lest We Forget" might well be the title of a class notebook in which pupils keep detailed records of experiments and activities. An honest, complete record of observations can be examined at any time to see what really happened. It is surprising how different from the written record a recollection can be!

Some activities, such as "Aged in Wood," do not call for extensive record keeping. Others suggest specific ways of keeping records. Drawing what he sees in "Brick Pebbles" encourages a pupil to observe more carefully. In "Squeeze Play," a column of numbered trials and times is needed for a graph from which the class can generalize. In "Stone Sizes," the record is a collection of objects themselves. In "Thunderstorm Paths," the record is a series of numbered marks on a map. Regardless of the manner in which they are made, however, records serve a single important purpose—to provide an efficient, orderly reminder of pupils' observations.

In activities such as "Living Fuzz," records of things like the kind of food in the bag are of obvious importance. Other records, such as those of temperature and moisture, may not seem important at the time, but are useful in answering questions that arise later. Questions themselves often are worth recording because they may suggest a different method of procedure, or a test of ideas.

Once records are made, they should be used. Pupils soon lose any sense of purpose in record keeping if their records become busywork and are not evaluated at the end of an activity.

By having pupils keep records, even simple ones, from the first grade on, you will help them to make record keeping a habit and an essential part of almost any science activity. Then when they ask, "How do we know?" or "What is the evidence?" their records will give the answer.

sun, moon, and stars

12

Since prehistoric times, man has been intrigued by the bright objects in the sky. His wonderment still continues, even with his more sophisticated understanding of what these objects are and why they appear and change as they do. How fortunate it is that his curiosity is not yet satisfied and that, with the aid of telescopes and other instruments, he carries on more energetically than ever the beautiful search for answers!

Children, too, are fascinated by the sun, moon, and stars. Their interest, moreover, becomes even keener when they have the opportunity and encouragement to *observe* them—when teaching is not confined strictly to the classroom and to traditional time slots, and when the emphasis is not placed on mere memorization.

Fundamental to man's comprehension of the universe are direct sensory experiences—and these each pupil has a right to have for himself. Those who do not have these experiences—though they memorize the distance to the moon, the size of the sun, and the name of the second-nearest star—can have little real appreciation of astronomy. Nor will they be able to acquire this appreciation merely from words, pictures, and models!

A telescope is not essential for teaching basic astronomy, nor is a planetarium or a transparent globe necessary. The teacher does not have to know a great deal of subject matter. What *is* needed, above all, is a willingness to go outdoors—first alone, and then with the class—and to *observe* the sun, moon, and stars, to note changes in their position and appearance, to make crude measurements, and to keep simple records. Then, along with doing these things, the teacher and pupils can use books, films, a planetarium, and other teaching aids to *supplement* the real experiences and to make them even more meaningful.

SOME IMPORTANT OBJECTIVES

ATTITUDES AND APPRECIATIONS TO BE ENCOURAGED:

Any person can gain a feeling of satisfaction and inspiration from observing the sun and moon and from recognizing familiar stars and patterns of stars.

There is a beautiful orderliness in the motions and the changes in appearance of the sun, moon, and stars.

One need not have expensive equipment or unusual scientific ability to learn a good deal of astronomy.

Astronomy makes a first-rate hobby, and for someone especially interested and inclined, it may become a fascinating life's work.

Things may not actually be as they appear; thus, the sun *seems* small, the moon often broken, all stars equally far away, and all of these bodies to be moving while the earth stays still.

Although modern man knows much about the universe, there remains a great deal more still to be discovered and understood.

There is no evidence that stars and other astronomical bodies affect the lives and fortunes of men in any supernatural way.

SKILLS AND HABITS TO BE DEVELOPED:

Noting the length and direction of sun-caused shadows, as well as their relation to the sun's position in the sky

Finding the moon in the daytime, naming its shape, and telling whether it is following or leading the sun across the sky

Recognizing that the moon changes shape in a regular sequence as it moves in relation to the sun, and predicting subsequent changes

Detecting the motions of stars, as well as of the sun and moon, in relation to objects on earth

Discerning that stars differ in brightness, color, twinkling, and the distance of shift in an hour's time

Locating the North Star and using it to tell direction

Identifying a few bright stars by name and recognizing some traditional constellations and other patterns of stars

Setting up a scale model of the moon and earth and adding to it, on the same scale, models of manmade satellites and the sun

Drawing ellipses of differing eccentricity, including one of the same shape as the earth's orbit around the sun

Using correctly such terms as axis, constellation, diameter, ellipse, gibbous, obtuse, phase, rotation, scale model, wane

FACTS AND PRINCIPLES TO BE TAUGHT:

Each clear day the sun seems to follow a path across the sky; this path gradually changes with the seasons, and is related to the time and place of sunrise and sunset, and the length of daylight.

The moon appears to move across the sky in the same general direction as the sun, but a little more slowly; its apparent shape is determined by its position with respect to the sun.

The stars also seem to move across the sky; unlike the few *planets*, they shift in unison and keep their same patterns.

The moon, like the earth, has only one side in sunlight at any time; its phases depend on how much of this sunlit half we see.

One way to account for the obvious motions of the sun, moon, and stars across the sky is to assume that the earth rotates.

The North Star shifts very little; this is interpreted to indicate that it is nearly in line with the earth's axis.

The moon gradually changes its position relative to the sun and stars, and this change is one evidence that it orbits the earth.

Careful surveying shows the moon to be about one-fourth as big as the earth in diameter and about 30 earth-diameters away.

Evidence indicates the sun is a hot ball with a diameter about 109 times that of the earth and about 12,000 earth-diameters away.

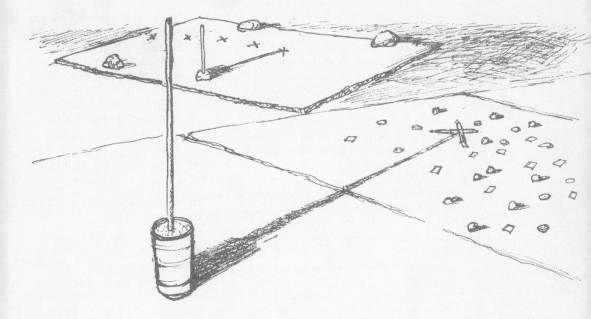

SHADOW
STICK

Pupils should become aware of how the sun appears to move across the sky during the day and of how its path changes during the year. A contest is an effective way to get them started.

Take the class outdoors on a sunny morning. Set a large can of soil or stones on a level walk, and stand a tall stick upright in it. Caution the pupils not to move the stick, even slightly. Then mark the tip of its shadow with chalk. *Where will the tip of the shadow be in 15 minutes?* Have each pupil mark the place he predicts with a pebble, button, or piece of tape. When the time is up, let the class check the markers. *Whose is closest?*

Let them try this again and then repeat it on subsequent days, at different times of the day, and with longer intervals. Also have them use the shadow of a flag-pole, lamppost, or tree.

With practice, pupils can become quite skillful in predicting the movement of shadows. Then let them keep a record of this movement by marking the tip of a shadow every hour, from early morning on, and connecting the marks with a curving line. A drinking straw standing in a lump of modeling clay on a large, level sheet of cardboard, weighted down, works well for this.

A class may make such a record on or near the first of each month, label the sheets, and save them. *How do the shadow curves for the various dates compare? Why is the one made in January so different from those made in October and in May?*

Older pupils may exchange shadow curves with classes in schools far to the south or north and even with some near the equator and in the southern hemisphere. This will help them to understand the relation of the angle of the sun's rays to climate and seasons, the concepts of the equator and the tropics of Cancer and Capricorn, and the reason for opposite seasons in the two hemispheres.

DAYTIME MOON

Children often think that the moon can be seen only at night. Actually, however, it is visible at some time during the daytime on most clear days. This they should discover for themselves. The experience is a basic one, yet it does not require a telescope or planetarium or even going out after dark.

Who can be the first to find the moon in the daytime? Let pupils look before school in the morning, while playing outdoors, during lunchtime, and at the end of the day. Then, when someone finds it, have him compare it with an assortment of "moons" cut from paper, choose one of matching shape, and stick it on a large calendar. In this way let pupils find the moon each clear day for a week or more and add paper "moons" to the record. On inclement days have them post symbols for clouds, rain, or snow.

Some sunny day, when the moon can be seen, take the class out, far from buildings. Give them some inexpensive, nonglossy balls. Let each pupil hold a ball at arm's length, directly in front of the moon in the sky, so that his hand does not hide the ball or cast a shadow on it. *Does the sunlit part of the ball appear similar in shape to the moon?* Pupils may need help in discerning the boundary between the sunlit and dark sides of the ball.

Caution pupils not to look directly at the sun!

How much of the ball's surface is lighted by the sun? How much of this sunlit part do we see? The same is true of the moon. If we see practically all of its sunlit side, we say it is *full*; if we see half of its sunlit side, in a *half phase*; if less than half, a *crescent*; and if more than half, in a *gibbous phase*. The shaded side of the moon usually cannot be seen because it is generally too dark—much darker than the shaded side of the ball, which is lightened by reflection from nearby objects.

DIRECTION OF SUN

MOON MOTIONS

As a continuation of "Daytime Moon," once again take the class outdoors on a clear day when the moon is visible, and have each pupil hold a tennis ball or other nonglossy ball directly in line with the moon. *How does the visible portion of the sunlit side of the ball compare, in shape, with the moon in the sky?*

Caution pupils not to look directly at the sun!

Now ask each pupil to move the ball slowly to the right or left and note any change in the appearance of its sunlit side. *Judging from this, would the* moon *look different if it were in another part of the sky? How would it appear if it were farther from the sun? Nearer the sun? On the other side of the sun?*

Which would be closer to the sun, the straight edge of a half moon or the round edge? Would the "horns" of a crescent moon point toward the sun or away from

it? Is this always true?

As observed under "Daytime Moon," the moon appears to change its shape from day to day— *to wax or wane. Does it, at the same time, change its position with relation to the sun? If so, is it getting closer to the sun or farther from it?* Let pupils check.

A good way to have pupils see the change in the relative position of the sun and moon is to have them extend one arm out straight toward the sun and the other toward the moon. They can then tell whether the angle between their arms is narrow or wide, a right angle or a straight angle, acute or obtuse. By making a record of this angle on successive days, they can note the change.

As the sun moves slowly across the sky during a day, does the moon follow behind it or lead it? Does the moon always do this?

The motion of the moon across the sky, as of the sun, may be explained by the rotation of the earth; its motion in relation to the sun may be attributed to the moon's orbiting the earth.

STAR
SHIFTS

These days it is often difficult enough to be able to *see* the stars, let alone to observe them move! Yet these experiences are ones which every child should have at first hand. Relegating them to a planetarium is a little like having

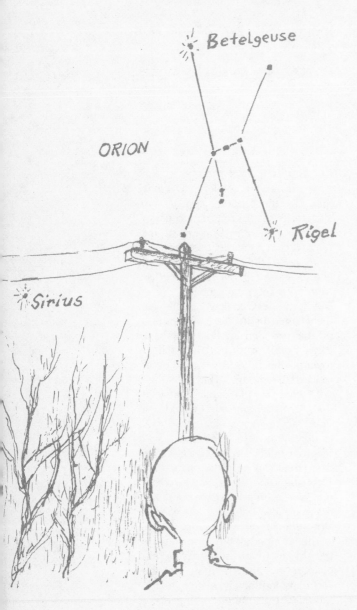

pupils experience the flight of wild geese by showing an animated cartoon!

To provide your pupils with an opportunity to watch *real* stars move, meet them on a clear evening, in an open area away from bright lights. Allow for bad weather by setting alternative dates. If school buses cannot pick them up, send notes home asking that each pupil be brought by a parent. The parents then share the responsibility and have a chance to learn, too.

Do not be discouraged if rather few show up. Those who are interested should not be deprived of a worthwhile experience. In any case, the number is likely to grow at subsequent meetings.

At the meeting ask everyone— both pupils and parents—to pick a star of his own and then to walk about until, while he is standing upright, it appears to touch the tip of a tree, the top of a pole, or some point on a television antenna. Then let him mark in some way the exact spot where he is standing.

Next, take just 15 minutes to point out a few constellations to the group. (See "Star Patterns.") Then ask each one to return to his spot, stand as before, and again sight on his star.

Now have them compare their observations. *What did the stars appear to do? In what direction? Did any seem not to shift? Did some stars rise or set during the 15 minutes? Is there any overall pattern to their motion?* (See "North-star Light.")

Finally, after another 15 minutes, let the group check their stars again. *Have the shifts continued? At this rate, about how far would the stars move in 1 hour? In 6 hours? In 24?*

NORTH-STAR LIGHT

It is surprising how few pupils (and adults!) are able to find the North Star. Many think it is very bright; some, brighter than any other star! On the contrary, it is quite ordinary-looking.

The outstanding thing about it is that, while all other stars appear to shift in the sky, the North Star changes its position very little. (See "Star Shifts.") It stays very close to the same point in the sky all night long (and all day, too), throughout the year! This is why it is so useful for finding direction.

It is easy to locate the North Star by using the Big Dipper as a guide. (See "Star Patterns.") An imaginary line connecting the two end stars in the bowl of the Dipper (the "Pointers"), when extended five times, almost touches the North Star. Even though the Big Dipper changes its position during the night and during the year, this relation to the North Star remains the same.

Having found the North Star, it is a good idea to mark its position. Stand a 4- or 5-foot stick, with a screw eye in its upper end, in a large can of soil or stones. Move them until a pupil, looking through the screw eye, sees the North Star exactly in line with the top of a pole, the corner of a roof, or a point on a television antenna. Then, without disturbing the stick, let pupils carefully check the position of the North Star throughout an evening. *Can any shift be detected?*

The beam of North-Star light that comes past the top of the pole and through the screw eye is almost parallel to the earth's axis. (See "Sunlit Earth.") A level line directly under this beam, running from the stick to the pole, points to true north or very nearly true north. (See "Bobby-pin Compasses.") For teaching these concepts it is useful to set up a permanent post having a screw eye in line with the tip of a flagpole and the North Star. An interested custodian will gladly do this.

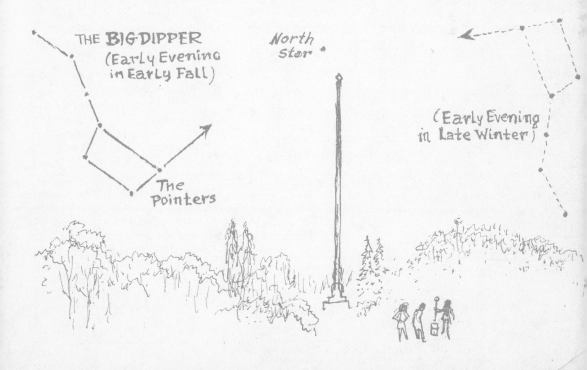

THE BIG DIPPER (Early Evening in Early Fall)

The Pointers

North Star

(Early Evening in Late Winter)

STAR PATTERNS

For thousands of years people have imagined stars to outline pictures, or patterns, in the sky. Finding these is still fun. Pupils should learn to recognize some of them, in part because they are useful in locating planets and other objects in the sky.

To help pupils learn some star patterns, arrange to meet them in a suitable place in the evening. (See "Star Shifts.") First let *them* try to imagine some pictures among the stars and, with a strong flashlight having a narrow beam, point them out to the group. Afterwards, trace out a few ancient, traditional patterns, or *constellations*. Inexpensive star finders are helpful for this, as well as sky charts in astronomy books. Note that some patterns, such as the Big Dipper, are visible throughout the year, while others, such as Orion, can be seen during some seasons only.

Later, have each pupil stand so as to line up a star with the top of a pole, chimney, or tree and then check it again from the same spot after a quarter hour or so. (See "Star Shifts.") *What does it do? Do the stars in a constellation all shift in unison and thus keep the same pattern, or does each move independently of the others?* What they appear to do can be explained more neatly by assuming the earth to rotate than by supposing the stars to be actually all moving in conformity.

Let pupils also see if they can agree on the order of brightness of a few stars in some constellation. This order is often indicated by letters of the Greek alphabet. Thus, *Alpha Orionis* is the brightest star in Orion; *Beta Orionis* is next bright.

What colors do stars show? Are any reddish stars visible? Bluish-white ones? Orange or yellow stars?

Are the stars twinkling? If so, which seem to twinkle more, stars near the horizon or those high in the sky?

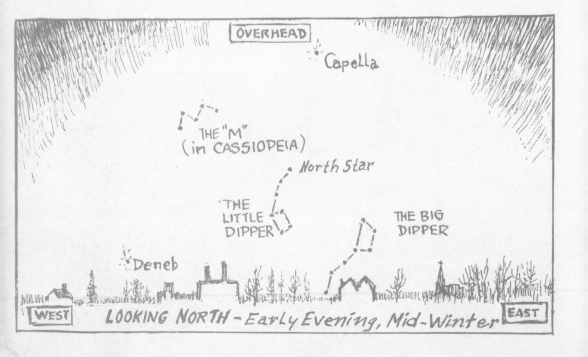

WEST — LOOKING NORTH – Early Evening, Mid-Winter — EAST

OVERHEAD — Capella — THE "M" (in CASSIOPEIA) — North Star — THE LITTLE DIPPER — THE BIG DIPPER — Deneb

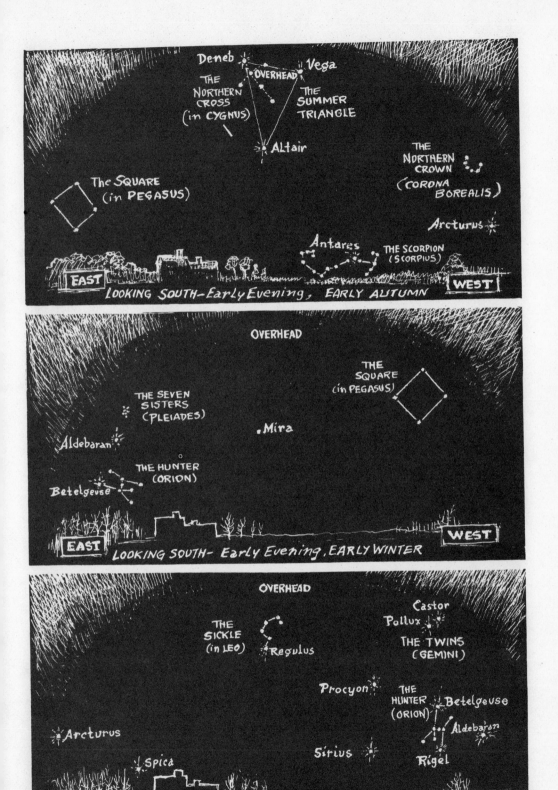

Deneb

Vega

OVERHEAD

THE
NORTHERN
CROSS
(in CYGNUS)

THE
SUMMER
TRIANGLE

Altair

THE
NORTHERN
CROWN
(CORONA
BOREALIS)

The SQUARE
(in PEGASUS)

Arcturus

Antares

THE SCORPION
(SCORPIUS)

EAST

WEST

LOOKING SOUTH—Early Evening, EARLY AUTUMN

OVERHEAD

THE
SEVEN
SISTERS
(PLEIADES)

THE
SQUARE
(in PEGASUS)

Mira

Aldebaran

THE HUNTER
(ORION)

Betelgeuse

EAST

WEST

LOOKING SOUTH—Early Evening, EARLY WINTER

OVERHEAD

Castor

Pollux

THE
SICKLE
(in LEO)

Regulus

THE TWINS
(GEMINI)

Procyon

THE
HUNTER
(ORION)

Betelgeuse

Arcturus

Aldebaran

Spica

Sirius

Rigel

EAST

WEST

LOOKING SOUTH—Early Evening, EARLY SPRING

SUNLIT EARTH

What must it be like to view the earth from far out in space? Where would its sunlit and dark sides be? Let your class find out by observing a globe in sunlight!

Take the class outdoors on a sunny day and set a globe where no shadows fall on it, preferably on grass or blacktop pavement to reduce unwanted reflection. Prop it up so that its axis points toward the North Star's position. (See "North-Star Light.") Then rotate it on its axis until the map of your state is at the highest part of the globe, parallel to the ground. Now the globe is in the same position as the actual earth, relative to the sun. *Where on the earth is it now daytime? Where is it dark?*

Stick a small lump of modeling clay on the globe to represent the location of your school. Stand a toothpick in the clay so it is straight up. *How does the direction of the toothpick's shadow on the globe compare with a flag-pole's shadow on the ground?*

Where do the sun's rays strike the globe at a right angle? Where are they now striking the actual earth at a right angle? To a person at this place, where would the sun be in the sky?

Some sunny day leave the globe outside all day and let the class see how its sunlit and dark parts change. *In what countries is the sun rising when it is nine o'clock where you are? Where is it setting at this time? What places have noon? Midnight? Where are other children eating breakfast now? Going to bed?*

It is good to put the globe outdoors on sunny days from time to time throughout the year. Then pupils can see how its sunlit and shaded halves, corresponding to the sunlit (daytime) and shaded (nighttime) sides of the actual earth, change with the seasons. Let them keep a record, by taking photographs or making sketches of the globe, for making comparison with the globe itself at later seasons.

TOWARD the NORTH STAR

MOON
MODEL

Pupils are excited by the idea of taking a trip to the moon. Seldom, however, do they have a correct notion of the distance involved. This is, in part, due to the grossly incorrect models and diagrams they so often see in school. To give them a truer concept, help them to set up an inexpensive scale model of the moon and earth, with true relative size and distance.

Use a globe to represent the earth. Then, for the moon, let pupils find a ball with a diameter slightly more than one-fourth the diameter of this globe. This is the correct ratio, since the diameter of the moon, almost 2,200 miles, is a little more than one-fourth that of the earth, slightly over 7,900 miles. (2,000/8,000 would be one-fourth.) Thus, if an 8-inch globe is used for the earth, a ball representing the moon should be slightly more than 2 inches across—2 3/16 inches is very close. Or, if the globe is 12 inches in diameter, a 3 1/4-inch

ball should be used. Pupils can easily find the diameter of balls with two boxes or blocks and a ruler. Slight inaccuracies are not serious.

Place the models at the ends of a string which is 30 times as long as the diameter of the globe. The string should be this long because the moon is, on an average, nearly 240,000 miles from the earth—a distance about 30 times the earth's diameter. Thus, with an 8-inch globe, the string should be about 240 inches, or 20 feet, in length. With a 12-inch globe, it should be about 30 feet long.

On this scale, how far from the globe should a speck be moved around it to represent a man-made satellite 100 miles high?

If a third ball were added to this model to represent the sun, what should its size and distance from the globe be? The sun's diameter is about 865,000 miles— 109 times the earth's diameter! Its distance from the earth averages almost 93,000,000 miles—nearly 12,000 times the earth's diameter!

CIRCUM-SUN RUN

Most people "know" that the path, or *orbit*, of the earth around the sun is an ellipse. If they were to sketch it, they would, as a rule, draw something like the ellipse in the sketch below, at A.

A little thought will show that this sketch is highly inaccurate. For one thing, if the orbit *were* of this shape, the earth's distance from the sun would change a great deal during the year. Consequently, the size the sun appears to be would vary considerably throughout the year, and so would the warmth the earth as a whole receives from the sun. This is not the case.

The fact that the apparent size of the sun varies very little during the year is evidence that the earth's orbit, even though elliptical, is practically circular. The false notion that it is *highly* elliptical probably stems, in part, from diagrams which picture the orbit as it would appear if viewed *obliquely*.

It is contrary to the spirit of science to indoctrinate pupils, blindly, with the concept that the earth travels around the sun once a year, in an elliptical orbit. It is sounder to wait until they are ready to understand and appreciate the *evidence* on which this idea is based. On the other hand, *if* the concept of the earth's orbit is taught at all, it should be presented correctly from the outset. In this case, there is value in having the pupils draw the *true* shape of the earth's orbit around the sun. This they can do according to the following directions:

Tie, with a *square* knot, a piece of thin string or thick thread snugly around a 3- by 5-inch card, kept flat, to make a loop exactly 3 inches long when stretched out. Next, stick a straight pin upright in the center of a flat sheet of thick corrugated cardboard at least 8 inches square. Lay the loop around the pin and pull it taut with the point of a ball-point pen or sharp pencil, held upright. Then, keeping the loop taut and flat

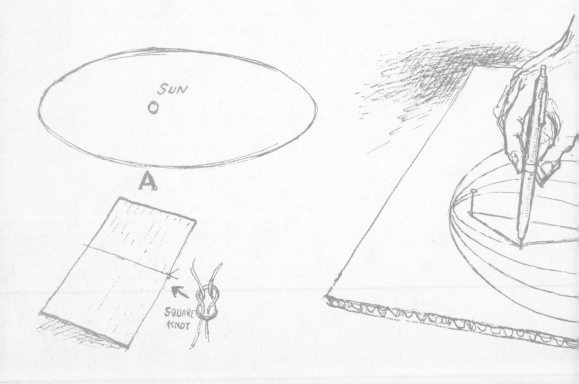

against the cardboard, move the pen around the pin. *Does the distance between the pin and the pen point change? What shape does the completed line have?*

Now stick a second pin into the cardboard, about two inches from the first. Place the loop around *both* pins, keep it taut with the pen point as before, and move the pen around. *This time is the completed figure a circle, or an ellipse?* Carefully measure its width in several different directions. Note that every place on it is at the same *total* distance from the two pins. The pins mark the two *foci* (singular, *focus*) of the ellipse.

Next, move the second pin still farther from the first, and draw another ellipse. Note that this one is more *eccentric* than the first. Then make a whole series of ellipses in this way, leaving the first pin in the same place, but placing the second farther and farther from it and then closer and closer to it. *What happens to the shape of the ellipses as the pins*

are placed farther apart? Closer together? Which of your ellipses has the greatest eccentricity? The least? What would the ellipse be like if the pins were very close together—so close that they are, in effect, merged into one?

Now you are ready to draw an ellipse that has the same shape as the earth's orbit. Turn the cardboard over, and stick both pins into it, this time just 3/32 inch apart. (This is, of course, halfway between 1/8 and 1/16 inch.) Again use the 3-inch loop. *What does the resulting ellipse look like? How do you know it is an ellipse, and not a circle?* Finally, remove one of the two pins and, using the remaining one and the loop, draw a true circle, preferably with a different color.

On this scale, with a 3-inch loop to represent the distance between the sun and the earth, 1/32 inch represents approximately one million miles. On the same scale, the sun, about 865,000 miles in diameter, would be a speck slightly smaller than 1/32 inch across—roughly the diameter of a pinhole. The sun is located at one focus of the earth's orbit; there is no visible object at the other. Therefore, you may label one of the pinholes —preferably the one at the center of the circle—the "Sun." On this scale, the earth would be microscopic. *According to this drawing, where in its orbit does the earth come closest to the sun? During which month is it in this part of its orbit?*

The other planets also orbit the sun in slightly elliptical paths. Each orbit has one focus at the sun, and the other elsewhere—different in each case.

representative
references

Note: Space precludes listing more than a few of the many good books which teachers and children will find helpful.

Counting and Measuring

Bendick, Jeanne: *How Much and How Many*, McGraw-Hill, New York, 1947. 179 pages. Upper.

Berkeley, Ethel: *Big and Little, Up and Down*, William R. Scott, New York, 1960. Unpaged. Primary.

Rockcastle, Verne: *Manual for Measurement Science*, Ohaus Scale Corporation, Union, N.J., 1965. 64 pages. Intermediate, upper.

Tannenbaum, Beulah, and Stillman, Myra: *Understanding Time*, McGraw-Hill, New York, 1958. 137 pages. Upper.

Air and Weather

Knight, David: *The First Book of Air*, Franklin Watts, New York, 1961. 65 pages. Intermediate, upper.

Riehl, Herbert: *Introduction to the Atmosphere*, McGraw-Hill, New York, 1965. 350 pages. Teachers.

Rockcastle, Verne: *Little Climates* (Cornell Science Leaflet), Cornell University, Ithaca, New York, 1961. 32 pages. Intermediate, upper.

Schneider, Herman: *Everyday Weather and How It Works*, McGraw-Hill, New York, 1961. 181 pages. Upper.

Zim, Herbert, and others: *Weather*, Golden Press, New York, 1957. 157 pages. Upper, teachers.

Water and Other Liquids

Lewis, Alfred: *This Thirsty World*, McGraw-Hill, New York, 1964. 94 pages. Upper, teachers.

Lynde, C. J.: *Science Experiences with Inexpensive Equipment*, Van Nostrand, Princeton, N.J., 1950. 266 pages. Upper, teachers.

Pine, Tillie, and Levine, Joseph: *Water All Around*, McGraw-Hill, New York, 1959. 48 pages. Intermediate.

Powders and Solutions

Brent, Robert: *The Golden Book of Chemistry Experiments*, Golden Press, New York, 1960. 111 pages. Upper.

Beeler, Nelson, and Branley, Franklyn: *Experiments in Chemistry*, Crowell, New York, 1952. 147 pages. Upper.

Freeman, Mae, and Freeman, Ira: *Fun with Chemistry*, Random House, New York, 1944. 59 pages. Upper.

Manufacturing Chemists' Association, Inc.: *Matter, Energy and Change*, Holt, Rinehart, and Winston, New York, 1960. 50 pages. Upper, teachers.

Rocks and the Land

Mather, Kirtley: *The Earth beneath Us*, Random House, New York, 1964. 320 pages. Upper.

Matthews, William, III: *Exploring the World of Fossils*, Childrens Press, Chicago, 1964. 153 pages. Upper, teachers.

Ramsey, William, and Burckley, Raymond: *Modern Earth Science*, Holt, Rinehart, and Winston, New York, 1965. 630 pages. Upper, teachers.

Sootin, Harry, and Sootin, Laura: *The Young Experimenters' Workbook (Treasures of the Earth)*, Norton, New York, 1965. 59 pages. Upper.

Zim, Herbert, and Shaffer, Paul: *Rocks and Minerals*, Golden Press, New York, 1957. 160 pages. Upper, teachers.

Plants and Animals

American Institute of Biological Sciences: *High School Biology* (B.S.C.S. Green Version), Rand McNally, Chicago, 1963. 728 pages. Teachers.

Ames, Gerald, and Wyler, Rose: *The Giant Golden Book of Biology*, Golden Press, New York, 1967. 99 pages. Upper, teachers.

Baranowski, Richard: *Insects*, Golden Press, New York, 1964. 103 pages. Upper, teachers.

Fenton, Carroll, and Pallas, D. C.: *Trees and Their World*, John Day, New York, 1957. 93 pages. Intermediate, upper.

Klots, Elsie: *The New Field Book of Freshwater Life*, Putnam, New York, 1966. 378 pages. Teachers.

Palmer, E. L.: *Fieldbook of Natural History*, McGraw-Hill, New York, 1949. 641 pages. Teachers.

Ravielli, Anthony: *Wonders of the Human Body*, Viking, New York, 1954. 125 pages. Upper.

Selsam, Millicent: *Play with Seeds*, William Morrow, New York, 1957. 93 pages. Upper.

Forces and Motions

Pine, Tillie, and Levine, Joseph: *Friction All Around*, McGraw-Hill, New York, 1960. 48 pages. Primary, intermediate.

Rockcastle, Verne: *Round and Round* (Cornell Science Leaflet), Cornell University, Ithaca, New York, 1964. 32 pages. Upper, teachers.

Ruchlis, Hy: *Orbit*, Harper, New York, 1958. 147 pages. Upper, teachers.

Sharp, Elizabeth: *Simple Machines and How They Work*, Random House, New York, 1959. 81 pages. Intermediate, upper.

Ubell, Earl: *The World of Push and Pull*, Atheneum, New York, 1964. 59 pages. Intermediate, upper.

Vibrations and Sounds

Baer, Marian: *Sound, an Experiment Book*, McGraw-Hill, New York, 1952. 125 pages. Upper.

Kettelkamp, Larry: *The Magic of Sound*, William Morrow, New York, 1956. 64 pages. Intermediate, upper.

Neal, Charles: *Sound*, Follett, Chicago, 1962. 32 pages. Intermediate.

Pine, Tillie, and Levine, Joseph: *Sounds All Around*, McGraw-Hill, New York, 1958. 48 pages. Intermediate.

Magnetism and Electricity

Adler, Irving: *Electricity in Your Life*, John Day, New York, 1965. 127 pages. Upper.

Beeler, Nelson, and Branley, Franklyn: *Experiments with Electricity*, Crowell, New York, 1949. 139 pages. Upper.

Branley, Franklyn, and Vaughan, Eleanor: *Mickey's Magnet*, Crowell, New York, 1956. 48 pages. Primary.

Podendorf, Illa: *The True Book of Magnets and Electricity*, Childrens Press, Chicago, 1961. 47 pages. Intermediate.

Lynde, C. J.: *Science Experiences with Ten-Cent Store Equipment*, Van Nostrand, Princeton, N.J., 1950. 262 pages. Upper, teachers.

Light and Other Radiations

Elementary Science Study: *Light and Shadows*, McGraw-Hill, New York, (in press). Primary.

Freeman, Ira: *All About Light and Radiation*, Random House, New York, 1965. 138 pages. Intermediate, upper, teachers.

Physical Science Study Committee: *Physics*, D. C. Heath, Boston, 1965. 668 pages. Teachers.

Rogers, Francis: *Lens Magic*, Lippincott, Philadelphia, 1957. 158 pages. Upper, teachers.

Ruchlis, Hy: *The Wonder of Light*, Harper, New York, 1960. 154 pages. Upper, teachers.

Heat and Temperature

Adler, Irving, and Adler, Ruth: *Heat*, John Day, New York, 1964. 48 pages. Intermediate, upper.

Pine, Tillie, and Levine, Joseph: *Heat All Around,* McGraw-Hill, New York, 1963. 48 pages. Intermediate.

Ruchlis, Hy: *The Wonder of Heat Energy,* Harper, New York, 1961. 186 pages. Upper, teachers.

Sootin, Harry: *Experiments with Heat,* Norton, New York, 1964. 93 pages. Upper.

Sun, Moon, and Stars

Dodson, R. S., Jr.: (Dr. Clyde Fisher's) *Exploring the Heavens,* Crowell, New York, 1964. 214 pages. Upper, teachers.

Skilling, William, and Richardson, Robert: *Sun, Moon and Stars*, McGraw-Hill, New York, 1964. 297 pages. Teachers.

Wyler, Rose, and Ames, Gerald: *The New Golden Book of Astronomy,* Golden Press, New York, 1965. 103 pages. Upper.

Zim, Herbert, and Baker, Robert: *Stars,* Golden Press, New York, 1956. 158 pages. Upper, teachers.

Star and Satellite Path Finder, Edmund Scientific Company, Barrington, N.J. (A chart for star-finding.)

General Teacher References

Beauchamp, Wilbur, and Challand, Helen: *Basic Science Handbook K–3,* Scott, Foresman, Chicago, 1961. 352 pages.

Blough, Glenn, and Schwartz, Julius: *Elementary-School Science and How To Teach It*, Holt, Rinehart, and Winston, New York, 1964. 640 pages.

Tannenbaum, Harold, and others: *Science Education for Elementary School Teachers,* Allyn and Bacon, Boston, 1965. 344 pages.

index